Mne

DATE DUE

GRAD	AUG 12 1982		
CMSU	AUG 15 1994		

GAYLORD PRINTED IN U.S.A.

D1060386

THE MECHANISM OF SPEECH

THE MECHANISM OF SPEECH

LECTURES DELIVERED BEFORE THE AMERICAN ASSOCIATION TO PROMOTE THE TEACHING OF SPEECH TO THE DEAF, TO WHICH IS APPENDED A PAPER

VOWEL THEORIES

READ BEFORE THE NATIONAL ACADEMY OF ARTS AND SCIENCES

ILLUSTRATED WITH CHARTS AND DIAGRAMS

BY

ALEXANDER GRAHAM BELL

SIXTH EDITION

FUNK & WAGNALLS COMPANY
NEW YORK AND LONDON
1914

CENTRAL MISSOURI STATE UNIVERSITY
Warrensburg, Missouri

COPYRIGHT, 1906, BY
ALEXANDER GRAHAM BELL
Printed in U. S. A.

PE1135
.B54
1907

CONTENTS.

9874

9874

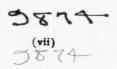

PREFACE TO SECOND EDITION.

These lectures upon the Mechanism of Speech were delivered at the First Summer Meeting of the American Association to Promote the Teaching of Speech to the Deaf, before an audience composed largely of persons professionally engaged in the work of teaching speech to deaf children.

In 1906 these lectures were for the first time collected in book form and reprinted by the Association, chiefly for the use of its members, but enough copies were struck off to allow of the presentation of the work to the general public in the hope that it would prove of interest to a larger circle of readers. This hope was realized and there is now a demand for another edition.

The first edition was printed during the author's absence in Europe, so that he had no opportunity of revising the proofs; and, unfortunately, in using the unfamiliar type representing Melville Bell's Speech-Symbols, the printers made quite a number of typographical mistakes. In this second edition advantage has been taken of the opportunity to correct these errors.

When the lectures were originally delivered the teachers present were encouraged to ask questions concerning difficulties experienced in imparting the power of articulate speech to deaf children. In this volume the questions and answers have been appended to the lectures, in the hope that the replies may be of assistance to other teachers engaged in this difficult and laborious work.

A paper by the author upon "Vowel Theories" is also appended, as the original publication is difficult to find, and the paper itself is out of print. This paper was read before the National Academy of Sciences, April 15, 1879, and appeared in the American Journal of Otology, Vol. 1, July, 1879. The experiments described were made with the phonograph in the form in which it was given to the world by Edison—a grooved cylinder covered with tinfoil; but still more conclusive results are obtained with the improved phonographs and graphophones of to-day.

ALEXANDER GRAHAM BELL.

WASHINGTON, D. C.,
May 24, 1907.

SYNOPSIS.

MELVILLE BELL'S SPEECH-SYMBOLS AS TAUGHT TO THE DEAF.

QUESTIONS.

THE THORAX AND LARYNX.

The thorax is the treasure-house of the human body,—a veritable strong-room, girt about with walls of bone for the protection of those precious organs the heart and lungs. Let us imagine ourselves for a moment inside the thorax, but first, with your permission, let us empty this safe-deposit vault of its valuable contents, so that we may have space for exploration.

We find ourselves in a dark room or vault with a door in the roof. The floor of this vault, instead of being firm and solid, is a soft membrane or muscle,—not flat like an ordinary floor, but dome-shaped like the top of an open umbrella. The door above is a sort of double trap door set at an angle instead of being flat, and opening upwards. But the most extraordinary thing about this room is, that the floor is in constant motion, heaving upwards and downwards in regular pulsations. The trap doors also are in motion; now they are opened so that a glimpse can be obtained of passages above, and now they come together with a quivering motion, opening and shutting with great rapidity, and causing a vibration that makes the whole thorax tremble. The walls also are in motion, the whole room alternately increasing and diminishing in size.

A membranous muscle when it contracts tends to become flat and tense; and many of us have had the idea that the diaphragm or dome-like floor of the thoracic cavity, in contracting becomes flat like the head of a drum. This idea is incorrect, for the central portion of the diaphragm is attached above by ligaments and tissues to the bony walls of the thorax, so that it is incapable of descent. The circumference or edge, also, is attached. When, therefore, the diaphragm contracts, the dome-like floor becomes somewhat conical in shape. As I picture the action in my mind, it is as though the dome of the capitol in Washington were to change into a cone somewhat like a blunt church spire.

When, then, the diaphragm contracts, the thoracic floor becomes tense and somewhat conical in shape, and the cavity of the thorax is thus enlarged. When the muscular fibres relax, the tense floor becomes loose and baggy, resuming its dome-like shape, and the space within the thorax then becomes less. Continuing our explorations we find that the front or chest wall of the thorax is capable of slight motion. By the operation of certain muscles, the ribs can be raised to a limited degree, so as to cause an increase in the circumference of the chest, and thus an expansion of the thoracic cavity. In animals which are prostrate gravity helps the expanding action, but in man, on account of his upright position, the weight of the bony framework renders a distinct effort necessary in order to elevate the chest wall, and relaxation of the muscles tends to collapse and consequent contraction of the thoracic cavity.

It will thus be seen that the interior capacity of the thorax can be increased; (1) by the contraction and consequent depression of the diaphragm; (2) by the elevation of the front wall of the chest; or, (3) by both actions performed simultaneously. When the interior capacity is increased, the air within the thorax expands to fill the increased space, thus becoming rarified. If the trap doors are open the denser air of the atmosphere then presses its way into the thorax to supply the partial vacuum. The act of inspiration is completed when the air pressures within and without the thorax are equal. If now the interior capacity of the thorax be diminished, the contained air by compression becomes denser than the air outside, and therefore tends to rush out, and the act of expiration is completed when the air pressures within and without are equal.

Exhalation can be effected; (1) by relaxation of the diaphragm which rises into its dome-like shape; (2) by relaxation of the muscles that raise the ribs, thus allowing the front wall of the chest to fall; or (3) by both processes performed simultaneously. We cannot, however, by any of these means produce that forcible expulsion of air that is requisite for speech, for relaxing muscles cannot exert much compressing power. What we need for speech is a forcible compression of the thoracic cavity. This can be effected by the abdominal or waist muscles. The contraction of these muscles produces a compressing effect upon the viscera, just as though a rope were passed around the waist and drawn tightly. This compression forces the viscera upwards against the under side of the diaphragm. The diaphragm is thus pushed up like a piston into the thoracic cavity, compressing the contained air. In this way forcible emission of air is caused by the contraction of the abdominal muscles, and these are the muscles that we employ in throwing out the voice. For example:—Prolong a vowel sound, suddenly increasing the force into a shout, a number of times in succession, without stopping the voice, thus:—ah, AH-ah-AH-ah-AH. At every shout a forcible contraction of the abdominal muscles can be felt by the hand, and the front wall of the chest is thrown upwards by the force of the compressed air within the thorax, pulsating outwards with every shout.

Alternate inspiration and expiration, result from alternate expansion and contraction of the thoracic cavity. This can be effected in two ways.

We can expand the cavity; (1) by using muscles that tend to raise the ribs and cause them to separate from one another slightly; and (2) by depressing the diaphragm.

We can contract the cavity; (1) by allowing the chest wall to fall, using muscles that tend to bring the ribs nearer together; and (2) by employing the abdominal or waist muscles.

Of these two possible modes of action, it will be seen that one involves the expenditure of less energy than the other. It is less laborious to breathe by using the diaphragm and waist muscles, than by moving the heavy bony framework of the chest.

When the diaphragm contracts, changing from the dome-like to the conical shape, it presses downwards upon the viscera, thus causing an expansion of the abdominal cavity. When the abdominal muscles contract, the circumference of the waist diminishes. Thus in natural breathing, produced by the alternate action of the diaphragm and the abdominal muscles, the circumference of the waist increases during inspiration, and diminishes during expiration.

I doubt the advisability of directing a pupil's attention to these motions, for his attempts at reproduction are often attended by ludicrous results. The end desired would, I think, be better attained by directing his attention to the chest, and not to the abdomen. Get the pupil to expand the chest and keep it continuously expanded even when breathing out. If the bony framework of the chest is kept raised and fixed, breathing can only be performed by the diaphragm and waist muscles ; and, as the pupil cannot help breathing, nature will work the proper muscles without his knowledge or will.

This effort of continuous expansion can only be sustained for a few minutes at a time without fatigue by persons unaccustomed to the exercise ; but if persevered in day after day the pupil can acquire the power of sustaining the chest wall continuously during his waking hours. The exercise usually results in a marked increase in the capacity of the chest. I have known of instances where the circumference of the chest has increased between two and three inches after a month's practice. When we consider that the thorax is the storehouse of the lungs, it is obvious that this increased capacity will be beneficial to health. Deaf children, especially, require exercises of this sort, because their lungs have not been as fully exercised as those of ordinary children.

I consider this exercise of chest expansion as more beneficial to pupils than the breathing exercises that are usually employed. Conscious regulation of the breath is to be deprecated for the following reason: the primary object of breathing is the oxygenation of the blood, and the getting rid of the products of combustion in the lungs. We take in air to oxygenate the blood. We exhale to get rid of carbonic acid gas and aqueous vapor. The proper time to take in breath cannot be dictated to a pupil without interfering with the primary function of the lungs. Nature gives the signal for inspiration when the blood needs oxygenation, and when we attempt to regulate the breath consciously we are apt to interfere with the circulation of the blood. Breathing exercises should be stopped the moment dizziness is produced, for that is nature's indication of a disturbance in the circulation.

Inspiration is utilized for the oxygenation of the blood, and expiration alone is employed in the production of speech. Observe the breathing of a person engaged in conversation at a time when he is unconscious of your observation. You will find that many words are articulated between each inspiration. The time taken for inspiration is instantaneous, whereas the duration of the expiration is very long. The breath comes in quickly, and goes out slowly. This means that the trap doors in the roof of the thoracic cavity are opened widely during inspiration, and closed so tightly during the act of speech, that only a fine stream of air can escape from the thorax. The prime requisite for speech is a store of compressed air, which can be let out little by little, as wanted. It is obvious that the air would escape with a gush unless restrained. The trap doors already alluded to, constitute the chief means by which a too rapid escape of air is prevented. These trap doors are known as the vocal cords, and they are contained in the larynx.

THE LARYNX.

Fig. 1.

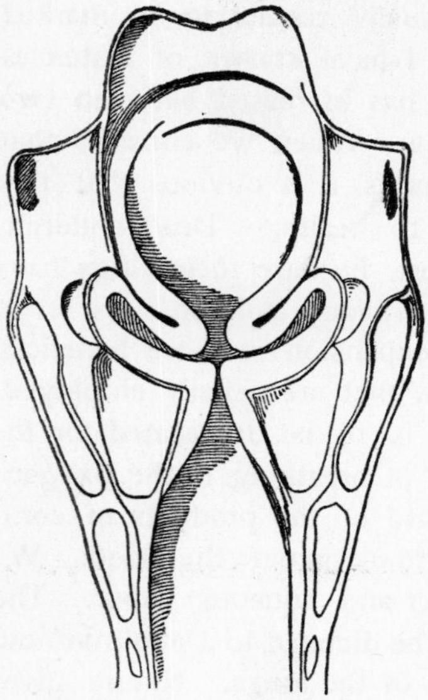

Vertical section of the Larynx as seen from behind.

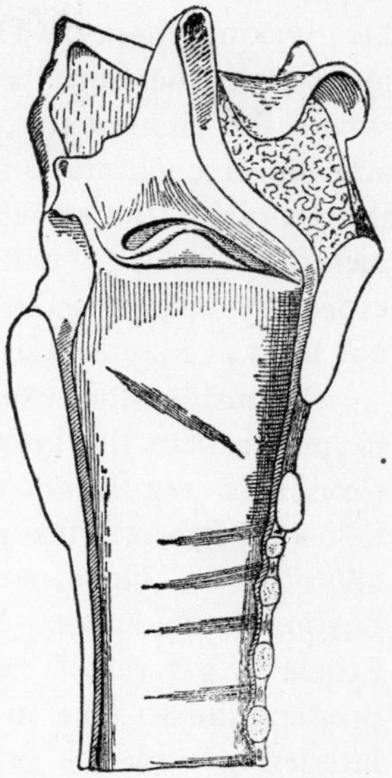

Vertical section of the Larynx as seen from the side.

The larynx may be considered as the guard-house of the lungs, —admirably adapted to protect them from injury. It consists essentially of a box, surmounted by a movable lid, called the epiglottis, which closes during the act of swallowing, to prevent food from

entering the lungs. Inside this box are two pairs of valves. The lower pair, called the true vocal cords, stand with their free edges upward, and the upper pair, known as the false vocal cords, hang with their edges downwards. The lower pair constitute the trap doors to which I have before alluded.

The specimens of the larynx which have been placed in your hands by Dr. Hewson, will have shown you that the vocal cords do not look like "cords" or strings at all—nor perhaps are they very suggestive of trap doors—they look more like lips. In fact, we may consider that we have a pair of lips within the larynx capable of approximation, with various degrees of tension.

The false vocal cords also resemble lips, but it is doubtful whether they can be approximated sufficiently to touch one another. If the lips of the throat are shut and the abdominal muscles are contracted, the air compressed within the thorax tends to blow the vocal cords apart. The muscular tension may be so adjusted as to allow the vocal cords to yield sufficiently to permit of the escape of a puff of air—the aperture closing again immediately and remaining closed until the pressure within the thorax causes the escape of another puff. In this way a regular series of puffs may be produced, the alternate opening and closing of the glottis constituting vibration of the vocal cords. The frequency of the vibration depends upon the tension of the vocal cords. The more tightly they are drawn, the more rapid will be the vibration produced.

With slow vibrations, distinct puffs of air can be heard, producing a sound known as "throat trill." If the glottis is opened and closed more than thirty-two times in one second, the ear fails to distinguish the individual puffs, and perceives only a continuous effect of a musical character denominated "voice." The pitch of the voice rises as the vibrations become more rapid.

There are two ways of varying the pitch of the voice, just as there are two ways of changing the pitch of a violin string. Observe the violinist tuning his instrument. He turns a peg at the end, thus tightening the string. At each increase of tension the pitch of the string becomes higher. When, however, he plays the instrument, the pitch is varied in a different manner. He presses his finger upon a string so as to permit only a portion of the string to vibrate, instead of the whole—and the pitch becomes higher. The shorter the vibrating portion, the higher is the pitch produced. In this case the tension of the string remains uniform.

In a similar manner variations of pitch in the voice may be produced by allowing a portion only of the vocal cords to vibrate, instead of the whole. Observations made by means of the laryngoscope, seem to indicate that the variations of pitch, in what is termed the "head register" of the voice, are produced in this manner; whereas, in the "chest register," the vocal cords vibrate as wholes, and the changes of pitch are produced by variations of tension.

Vocal cords vibrating in part.

Vocal cords vibrating as wholes.*

Dr. Hewson, during the course of his lecture, gave utterance to rather a startling remark. If I understood him correctly, he expressed the opinion that some of the vowel sounds are formed in the larynx, and not in the mouth. I cannot agree with him in this opinion, although I am aware that he can quote authorities in support of his position. For example: Dr. E. M. Moore, of Rochester, N. Y., has published an account of the following case:† Some years ago Dr. Moore attended a man who had attempted suicide by cutting his throat. The cut was immediately above the thyroid cartilage, shaving off the epiglottis at its base. The wound resulted in an oval opening, two inches long by three quarters of an inch wide. The man was able to talk at any time by bending his head forward and temporarily closing the opening. When the head was thrown back he lost the power, but Dr. Moore noticed that under such circumstances he could pronounce vowel sounds like ah, oh, etc. The doctor was surprised at the clearness and distinctness of the vowel effects, for the sounds seemed to emanate from the yawning wound in the throat, and not from the mouth. Struck by this circumstance, the worthy doctor made a unique experiment. He introduced into the wound a sheet of buckskin, so placed as to prevent the possibility of any air passing from the larynx into the mouth. The only outlet left for the breath, was the yawning wound. He then asked the man to repeat the alphabet, A, B, C, etc. Dr. Moore found that under these circumstances, certain vowel sounds could be distinguished, and he came to the conclusion that these vowels were formed in the larynx, and not in the mouth.

This conclusion would be more reliable if he had shown that the man could pronounce these vowels with his mouth shut. Of course, if the vowels heard were really produced in the larynx alone, the closure of the lips would have made no difference in the

---

* These cuts are reproduced from "Voice, Song, and Speech."

† See Transactions of the New York State Medical Society, 1872, pp. 276-282.

effect. Whereas, if the ordinary theory is correct, that vowel quality is due to the resonance of the mouth cavities, then the closure of the mouth passage, at both ends, would have been fatal to the effect.

I understand that during the course of the experiment, the man moved his mouth as though he were speaking; and Dr. Moore simply took precautions to prevent the passage of air through the mouth. The mouth positions for the vowels were, therefore, assumed, and the mouth would then, in effect, be a resonator, tuned to the vowel positions, held near a sounding body—the larynx. Under such circumstances, resonance effects should be produced without the actual passage of air through the mouth, just as an ordinary resonator, when properly tuned, becomes sonorous when held near a vibrating tuning fork.

I cannot look upon the experiment as by any means conclusive; and I know of no other facts to support the hypothesis that any of the vowels are formed in the larynx, independently of the mouth.

A number of years ago Dr. McKendrick, of Glasgow University, afforded me an opportunity of examining the speech of a man whose larynx had been excised. The patient had been supplied with an artificial substitute for the larynx, made, I think, of dentist's rubber. As there were no vocal cords, the man could only speak in a sort of whisper, which was barely audible. A small aperture had been left in the front part of the rubber substitute into which the man slipped a metal reed, taken from a harmonium or small parlor organ. Upon then attempting to speak, the reed was thrown into vibration by the air from the lungs, and a good sonorous voice resulted, —resembling the natural voice to a remarkable and startling degree. The patient spoke with a broad Scotch accent, and his articulation was simply perfect. Very little peculiarity could be detected in the artificial voice excepting that it was monotonous and without inflection. The speech was so natural in quality that it was difficult to realize that the source of sound was a metal reed inserted into the throat.

The man was a machinist by trade, and he employed his spare time in manufacturing reeds for himself. He had quite an assortment for experimental purposes, and he let me hear the effect of reeds of various sizes and materials. He could change his voice from bass to tenor, and from tenor to soprano at will, by employing suitable reeds.

The point to which I would direct your attention is this:—that the vowels were all perfectly produced, although the larynx had been excised.

We have seen that a metal reed can be used in place of the vocal cords; and I am inclined to think that the real larynx, if detached from the body and operated by means of a wind chest or organ bellows, would produce an effect more resembling the sound of a beating reed, than the human voice. The quality or "timbre" of the human voice, I believe, is due in a very minor degree to the vocal cords, and in a much greater degree, to the shapes of the passages through which the vibrating column of air is passed. As the shape of the passage above the vocal cords controls the quality or *timbre* of the voice, we may be sure that the false vocal cords exert some influence upon the quality of the voice, especially if they are capable of approximation, a point I am unable to decide. The ventricles, also, the spaces between the true and false vocal cords on either side, should, theoretically, exert an influence upon the quality of the voice, for they constitute two small resonance-chambers, situated close to the source of sound. In the howling monkey the ventricles are expanded into pouches, and the characteristic howl produced by the creature is due to the resonance of air in those chambers.

In the case of the Scotchman at the Glasgow University, the pitch of the artificial voice produced was undoubtedly due to the reed employed, but the quality of the voice, and the consonant and vowel effects were due to the passages above, through which the vibrating column of air was passed.

I have already directed your attention to the case reported by Dr. Moore of Rochester, New York, in which he claimed that certain vowels are formed in the larynx and not in the mouth. Dr. Moore directed my attention to the case of another patient of his which seems to prove the converse proposition. * Dr. Moore had performed upon this man the operation of tracheotomy. At the time I saw the patient he had for over twenty years been dependent for life upon air supplied through a silver tube inserted in the trachea. The glottis had become completely closed and no air could be forced through the larynx into the mouth. The strange feature of the case was that under these circumstances the man could talk. Of course the speech was peculiar on account of

---

* Case of Edward Matthews. See Transactions of the New York State Medical Society, 1872, pp. 276-282.

the absence of voice, but there was no difficulty in understanding it. In this case the air which was moulded into speech came not from the lungs, but from the pharynx. If we close the lips tightly and compress the air in the mouth and make an effort to blow, the pharynx expands under the pressure of the confined air, just as a rubber ball would expand if you were to blow into it. Upon opening the lips the contraction of the pharynx causes a sudden puff of air. A puff of air of this character can be produced even though the glottis is closed. By long practice this man had acquired such expertness in the use of the muscles about the pharynx that he could produce explosive effects of this kind which could be distinctly heard at a distance. When he spoke, the consonants were formed with very great firmness, and the removal of the consonant position resulted in a puff of air through the vowel positions assumed by the mouth, so that the puff had vowel quality sounding like a whispered vowel. I can imitate the character of his speech so that you may understand, more clearly than I can describe it, the nature of his articulation.

The point that I would have you observe is, that in this case vowel effects were unmistakably produced, although no air passed through the larynx into the mouth.

Dr. Hewson: Do I understand you to say that this individual who had the larynx closed, made audible speech?

Dr. Bell: Yes, sir; quite audible speech.

Dr. Hewson: I merely wish to make a statement from actual surgical experience that, in cases where the operation of tracheotomy has been performed, it is impossible to make any sound under such circumstances, unless the finger is placed over the tube in the trachea. Now, of course, that may be due to the condition which you have already indicated; that is, that the speech was produced by this individual by long practice. Now it is possible for people to speak when that tube is closed, even though the principal part of the vocal apparatus is lined with diphtheric membrane. There is some sort of sound made, at least, but there is no audible speech. The remark I made some time ago about the vowel sounds being made in the larynx, I will amend by saying that of course the experiments that you have had the opportunity of seeing, had not come to the notice of either myself or the gentlemen who have preceded me, in making statements in text-books from which I have quoted. Your experience, I believe, is very unique; because I have never heard of any one who had been able to see the experiments, made as you have detailed them to-day. With reference to the closure of the uppei part of the vocal apparatus by diphtheric membrane, and the introduction of a tube into the trachea; I may say that in order that any sound may be produced at all, the tracheal tube must be closed. Now, if the parts above, are almost closed by the diphtheric membrane, no sound is produced. However, I can readily see, from a knowledge of the muscular tissue surrounding the parts, that such sounds could be produced as you have detailed in this individual.

DR. BELL: In the case of this individual I have just mentioned, no air could pass up into the mouth, under any circumstances. The aperture in the windpipe remained open, and, all the time he was speaking, air gushed out of the tube in his throat, forming a whistling accompaniment to his speech.

MISS YALE: Dr. Bell, I have a number of questions here for you to answer.

DR. BELL: The first question is: "Is it possible to constrict the false vocal cords?" I think that Dr. Hewson will be more competent than I am to answer that question.

DR. HEWSON: I cannot conceive of any muscular fibres constricting the ventricular bands, or false vocal cords.

MR. CROUTER: How was it with the Scotchman, Dr. Bell?

DR. BELL: There were no vocal cords in the case of the Scotchman, the vocal cords were represented by a harmonium reed.

I hardly know how to commence on the stream of questions you have set for me. They appear to be of very great importance, and I should be very glad if I can be of any assistance to teachers here in answering them. I may, perhaps, group them so as to answer two or three at one time.

(1) "Please illustrate the development of *ng*."

(2) "Dr. Bell develops non-vocal *r* from *th;* please demonstrate."

(3) "How would you develop ***sh***?"

I will take up these in one group. In difficult cases you will find manipulation of the tongue of great assistance: and I think that this series of questions may be answered by showing you how to manipulate the tongue; and by directing your attention to the nature of the changes, you can produce by manipulation. You can push a position further back, and you can enlarge an aperture by manipulation; but you cannot do the converse. If, then, your pupil cannot pronounce a given sound, let him give a sound of similaformation but further forward in the mouth; then push the position back. For example; take the cases specified in the questions. (1.) The pupil cannot pronounce *ng*. Now, suppose he *can* pronounce *n* — a sound of similar formation but formed further forward in the mouth. Take a manipulator (for example; a paper cutter), and hold it in the pupil's mouth so as to cover the top or front part of the tongue. Now tell the pupil to say *n*. The point and front of the tongue being fettered, the back of the tongue alone is free to rise; and the attempt to say *n* results in *ng*. Now give the pupil a hand-mirror and tell him to keep his tongue still when you withdraw the manipulator. In most cases the pupil is at once able to pronounce *ng*, but in difficult cases it is advisable to get him to manipulate his tongue for himself, watching the effect in a hand-mirror.

(2) Your pupil cannot pronounce non-vocal *r*, but is able to give *th*. Place the manipulator under the tongue, and gradually lift the point of the tongue, while the pupil tries to sound *th*. The sound changes to a hiss, somewhat like *s*, then as the tongue is raised higher the sound becomes more like *sh;* and if lifted still higher, it becomes non-vocal *r*. When the correct position is reached, the point of the tongue is against the inner part of the upper gum—just where the palate commences to arch—with an aperture over the centre.

(3) The pupil cannot pronounce *sh*. Let him pronounce *th*. Place the manipulator over the tip of the tongue and push the tongue gradually back. The sound changes first to *s*, and then to *sh*. If pushed too far back, it becomes *yh* (*h* in the word *hue*); and if still further back, the German *ch* (back-centre aperture).

Another question is, "What would you do with a pupil who gives *ng* too far back?" I don't quite understand this question, for you can't get *ng* too far back. You can get *k* and *g* too far back, and these are very common defects. In such cases the back of the tongue is placed against the back of the pharynx instead of against the soft palate, but such a position cannot produce an *ng* sound, because the depression of the soft palate would not admit air into the nasal passages, the shut position being below the soft palate. It is very difficult to correct a position that is too far back. You can push a position further back, but you can't pull it forward! I think the best plan is to start anew. Take a position too far forward in the mouth, and push the tongue backwards to the correct position. For example; where you have *k* too far back, take *t;* let the pupil try to pronounce *t*, while you hold the manipulator over the tongue so as to prevent any portion from rising, excepting the back. In this way you will be sure of a good *k*, if the pupil does not know what you are aiming at. By vocalizing the *k* you get *g*. (Dr. Bell illustrated his remarks by manipulating the tongue of a deaf pupil.)

The next question is, "Please demonstrate that intelligible speech does not depend upon perfect vowel positions." I shall read a few sentences from a book, substituting for each vowel sound a mere indefinite murmur of voice. You observe that the articulation, though, of course, very peculiar, is perfectly intelligible.* We may learn from such an experiment as this, that consonants are much more important elements than vowels. Intelligibility of speech mainly depends upon the correct pronunciation of consonants. We could manage to get along very well with only one vowel sound, if indefinite enough, and yet make ourselves understood. I don't mean to advise you to teach speech of this character to your pupils, but many of you may be encouraged to know that very imperfect vowel sounds will not prevent your pupils from being understood by relatives and friends. Consonants are much more easily acquired than vowels, and all pupils who can pronounce the consonants correctly can acquire a useful articulation, even though they murder the vowels. That is, their speech will be intelligible to hearing people, and therefore useful as a means of communication, even though it may not be very pleasant to hear. Too much effort, I think, is made to impart a niceness of pronunciation that is not appreciated by the outside world.

When I first entered upon the work of articulation teaching, I was very proud of the pronunciation of some of my congenitally deaf pupils. They had been drilled upon the elements and were able to pronounce words and sentences written in Visible Speech with absolute correctness, slowly, it is true, but with perfect elementary sounds. To my great mortification, however, I found that

---

* Read the following passage aloud, giving an indefinite murmur of the voice for each dash, and the passage will be intelligible:—

- p-nt-d t- th- c-t -nd th-n t- -ts n-m -nd -nd-v-rd t- m-k h-m -n-rst-nd th- m-n-ng -v th- r-t-ng - -ls- t-t h-m t- sp-l th- w-rd -n h-s f-ngg-rs. -v-th-ng th-t h- d-d w-s p-rf-rmd w-th - p-nd-r-s s-rt -v -mf-s-s th-t w-d h-v m-d - p-rs-n -nf-m-ly-r w-th th- d-f s-p-z th-t h- n- -l -b-t -t.—*From the Annals for January, 1891, p. 45.*

You may substitute for the (-) any large aperture vowel, such as *u* in *up*, *er* in *her*, *o* in *on*, or even *a* in *cat*, without destroying intelligibility.

visitors generally preferred the imperfect gabble of some semi-mute to the elocutionary speech I had labored to impart. In those days I had a very poor opinion of the visitors, but I have since come to the conclusion that I myself was somewhat at fault. My aim was wrong. At that time I had the mistaken idea that it was hardly worth while teaching articulation at all, unless I could teach my pupils to *speak well.* My ear was sensitive to every mispronunciation, and I was constantly correcting my pupils for errors that were not even noticed by visitors to the school.

Our object is not to train elocutionists, but to help deaf children to make themselves understood. Intelligibility is of far greater importance than perfection. By all means let us get as perfect a pronunciation as we can, but do not let us spend much time on minor details of pronunciation that are of no consequence to intelligibility. Let us aim, not to get the speech of the elocutionist, *but the speech of the people among whom the children live.* Judged by the standard of the elocutionist, how many of the hearing people of the world talk well? Very few, and yet their speech is of inestimable value to them in all the relations of life.

Now, I hardly think it worth while attempting to teach the mass of the deaf to talk better than other people. Let us be satisfied with speech like that which we ourselves employ without troubling ourselves about niceties of articulation that might be all very well in an orator or public speaker, but which would be of no practical benefit to a deaf child in his own home. Observe your own utterance and the utterances of your friends, and you will find that half your syllables are pronounced in a slipshod fashion that would make an articulation teacher shudder if given in the same manner by a deaf child. Take such little words as *and* or *of.* Who gives them their proper dictionary pronunciation in actual speech? No one but the deaf child. We pronounce them somewhat as though they were spelled *und* or *uv.* You *und* I; a cup *uv* tea. No one says *thee* boy, *Ann* apple, or *eh* pear in conversation. The obscure sound is heard, and our utterance is more like *thu* boy, *un* apple, *u* pear. The same indefiniteness of vowel sound is characteristic of all our unaccented syllables. Why, then, need we be particular about the pronunciation of the unaccented syllables in such words as, comfortable (kumf-t-ble), lesson (les-n), silent (sil-nt), sentence (sent-nce), workman (workm-n), different (dif-r-nt), above (-buv), forgot (f-got), etc. Any sort of indefinite vowel sound will pass muster in these syllables if only softly uttered.

We are training our children to talk to ordinary people, not to elocutionists. There are certain points that must be attended to in order that the speech may be satisfactory to ordinary people; but in regard to other points, great latitude may be allowed.

Consonant elements and the vowels in accented syllables must be properly pronounced, but the vowels in unaccented syllables may be uttered in any sort of indefinite way without offending the ordinary ear. Accent and rhythm, I think, are of more importance than exact pronunciation.

In Visible Speech the voice symbol (ı) is used to indicate an indefinite vowel sound like *er* in the word her, or like the *er* sound used by public speakers to fill up gaps in their sentences—when—er—they are not—er—very—er—er—sure—er—what they want to say. This indefinite vowel sign I consider a perfect God-send to the teacher of articulation, enabling him to get rid of half the labor of articulation teaching. In spelling phonetically the vast majority of the vowel sounds in the unaccented syllables may be represented by this indefinite voice mark; and it may also be substituted everywhere for glide *r*. I would recommend those who do not use Visible Speech to use a dash.

Ordinary people who know nothing of phonetics or elocution have difficulty in understanding slow speech composed of perfect elementary sounds, while they have no difficulty in comprehending an imperfect gabble if only the accent and rhythm are natural. Too much labor is bestowed upon unaccented syllables. Any child can give an indefinite vowel sound that may be combined rapidly with consonants. I have seen a teacher puzzling herself over the word *comfortable*. The first syllable gave no difficulty, but the second syllable was not pronounced easily by the child. There was an attempt on the part of the pupil to give long ō, as in pole, followed by a consonant *r* of an exaggerated kind, and the teacher was trying to get the pupil to substitute *aw* for *o*. With regard to the last syllable the teacher was puzzled to decide whether the vowel should have the sound of *a* in table, *a* in cat, or *a* in ask. Now the fact is that the exact vowel sounds in the unaccented syllables are of no earthly consequence. An ordinary ear will accept any sort of indefinite sound as good speech, if the word is uttered rapidly with due accent on the first syllable. Even an elocutionist would not ask for a consonant *r* in the second syllable. He would simply demand a gliding of the tongue towards the position for *r;* but ordinary people do not give an *r* of any sort in a large proportion of cases, and it is certainly the case that glide *r* may be ignored in teaching a deaf :hild and taught simply as voice, without any ordinary person noticing any peculiarity, so that in the word "comfortable" the second syllable may be given as, *f* followed by the indefinite voice sign. (Ɜı, *f*–) So also with the vowel in the last syllable. The whole word, therefore, might be written ɑ]ɘƷıƱıɘω or kumf-t-bl. Pronounce the first syllable with due deliberation and care, and give tbe others rapidly and carelessly, and it will be satisfactory.

Dr. Williams: With indefinite vowel sounds, is there not a danger of carrying that too far so as to get indefiniteness?

Dr. Bell: You don't want to do that with accented vowels. However, it is the consonants that give intelligibility to speech. You may give every vowel indefinitely; but if the consonants are definite, you get intelligibility. If the accented vowels are given correctly, the unaccented vowels may be jumbled up somewhat.

Dr. Williams: But if they get into the habit of giving the vowel sound in that indefinite way, won't they carry it into the accented vowels?

Dr. Bell: Well, they might, just as we do. Of course, the better articulation you can get the better; but allow me to say that in ninety-nine out of a hundred persons you meet in ordinary society, that indefinite sound is carried into a great many accented syllables and also into nearly all the unaccented syllables.

The next question is, "In a whisper, are the vocal cords lax or tense?" In the case of a whisper there is a constriction; there is an obstructicn to the passage of air ir the glottis. The vocal cords are not adjusted so as to permit of a definite musical vibration, so that the obstructtion results in a rustling sound that we term "whisper."

Prof. Binner: You mean constriction of the vocal cords?

Dr. Bell: Yes, a constriction of the glottis — the space between the vocal cords.

THE PHARYNX AND MOUTH IN THEIR RELATION TO SPEECH.

In my last lecture I told you about a man with a harmonium reed in his throat, in place of vocal cords. Now, ordinarily, there is vast deal of difference between the sound of a harmonium, and the sound of the human voice, and yet in this case the reed produced the effect of a human voice when the man spoke. To the ear, therefore, it made all the difference in the world, whether the reed was vibrated outside or inside the man's throat. Now, we have no reason to suppose that the thorax and lungs operated in any different way from the wind chest of a harmonium. They simply supplied air to set the reed in vibration. The difference of effect, therefore, must have been due to the parts above the reed. In other words, the pharynx, mouth, etc., were the agencies involved in changing the harmonium effect into a human voice. Consider for a moment, the nature of the difference between the sound of a harmonium reed and a sound of similar pitch sung by the voice. The same note may be played upon a piano, a violin, a flute, or a trumpet, and yet each sound has an individuality of its own. We can tell by the ear, at once, which instrument is used, although all the notes may be alike in pitch, and equally loud. The sounds differ from one another in "character," "quality" or "timbre," and it will thus be understood that the pharynx, mouth, etc., affect the quality or timbre of the voice.

We can recognize that every sound possesses the elements of pitch, loudness, and quality. It matters not whether the sound be produced by the human voice, by a musical instrument, by the rustling of leaves, or by a knock upon the door—it has a certain loudness, a certain pitch and a certain character, or timbre of its own, by which we recognize it from other sounds of similar pitch and loudness.

Now, when we study the production of voice, we find that these three characteristics originate principally in three different parts of the vocal apparatus.

(1) The pitch of the voice is determined by the vocal cords.

(2) The loudness by the abdominal or expiratory muscles; and

(3) The quality or timbre by the parts above the vocal cords.

1. The lips of the glottis open and close with great rapidity, and the frequency of the vibration is mainly determined by the tension of the vocal cords.

2. Air escapes from the lungs through this vibrating glottis in a series of puffs, and the force of emission is chiefly determined by the action of the abdominal or expiratory muscles.

3. The upper part of the larynx, together with the pharynx, nares, and mouth, constitutes a passage-way, or tube, of variable size and shape, through which the vibrating current of air is passed. It is here that the voice is moulded, so to speak, on its way to the ear, and the shape of the passage-way largely determines the quality or timbre of the voice.

You can produce a crude voice-like sound by the vibration of the lips of the mouth. Press your lips very firmly together while you blow air between them, so as to cause the edges to vibrate. The sound produced is not very pleasant, and resembles more than anything else the hum of a bee, or the buzz of an imprisoned fly. But place the buzzing lips at the end of a tube—for example a trumpet—and at once the quality changes. Out come the clear ringing tones so familiar to us in a brass band! In this case the source of sound is found in the vibration of the lips, but the timbre or metallic quality is due to the trumpet.

In a somewhat similar manner the passage-way or tube, through which the voice is passed, affects the quality of the sound produced by the lips of the throat; and if we could decapitate a singer in the midst of a song, so as to hear the sound produced by his vocal cords alone, I fancy we should find as great a change in the quality of the voice, as we do in the sound produced by the lips when the trumpet is removed. The beauty of the voice would be gone, and you would simply have a reed-like effect.

In the case of the trumpet, the character of the tube affects not only the quality, but the pitch of the sound produced. For example: If you lengthen the tube, the lips vibrate more slowly, and the sound becomes lower in pitch. In the instrument of speech, however, the lips of the glottis are so admirably adapted for independent vibration, that changes in the passage-way do not affect their rate of vibration, but simply change the quality of the resulting sound.

A number of years ago I visited a large school for the deaf, and taught all the pupils to use their voices. In a few cases the effect was decidedly unpleasant, the voice resembling somewhat the cry of a peacock. The effect, indeed, was so unnatural and distressing to the ear that some of the teachers expressed the opinion that the vocal cords had been affected by the disease that had caused deafness. They thought, therefore, that it would hardly be worth while attempting to teach these children to speak. Knowing that the quality of the voice is chiefly determined by the shape of the passage through which it is passed, I did not consider it necessary to assume a defect in the vocal cords, but rather sought the cause of the peculiarity in some constriction of the passage-way higher up than the vocal cords.

I was careful to avoid discouraging the pupils by any expression of disapproval, so they were entirely unconscious of the fact that their voices were unpleasant. They had no hesitation, therefore, in repeating the disagreeable sound as often as I desired; and I encouraged them to repeat it a great many times, so that I might study the effect and become familiar with the sound. I then found it possible to imitate the effect myself. This was proof positive that the existence of the peculiarity was quite consistent with the possession of perfect vocal organs. Having acquired the ability to repeat the effect, I set myself to work to find out what I did with my mouth during the production of the sound. I could feel a constriction somewhere in the back part of the mouth, and therefore examined my vocal organs in a hand mirror while I depressed the tongue so as to exhibit the whole of the pharynx. At once the cause of the peculiarity became manifest. The muscles constituting the side walls of the pharynx were seen to be forcibly contracted, and they were approximated so closely together as almost to touch. After a little practice I found myself able to move these muscles at will without making any sound. Then I tested the effect of the motion upon the quality of the voice. When the muscles were relaxed and the cavity of the pharynx expanded the quality of the voice was good, but the moment the side walls of the pharynx commenced to approach one another (see dotted lines in Fig. 2.), the character of the voice changed. It acquired a pecul-

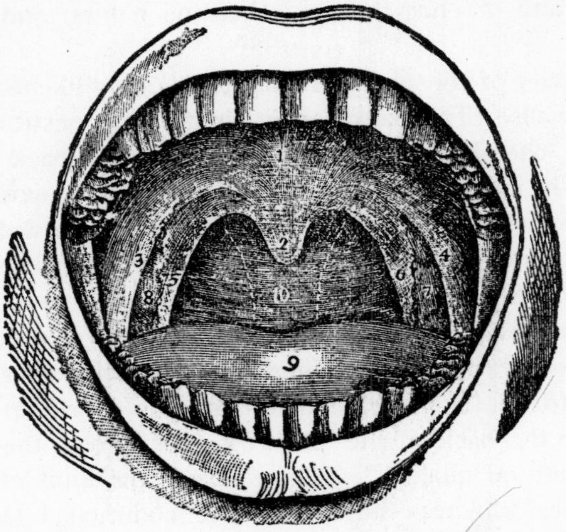

Fig. 2.*

1. Soft palate. 2. Uvula. 3, 4. Anterior pillars of the soft palate. 5, 6. **Posterior** pillars of the soft palate. 7, 8. Tonsils. 9. Tongue. 10. Back of the pharynx.
The posterior pillars of the soft palate (5, 6,) are capable of approximation, as shown by dotted lines.

iar metallic ring, somewhat like the tone of a brass musical instrument. The effect became more and more disagreeable as the side walls approached, until the peculiarly distressing effect was produced, which I have likened to the cry of a peacock. Having gained this information I attempted to improve the voices of the children. For this purpose I gave them hand mirrors and taught them to depress their tongues so as to render visible the soft palate and back of the pharynx. I then made them look into my mouth while I silently contracted and expanded the pharynx. After some practice they were able to imitate the action.

I then placed my hands on my throat while I repeated the exercise with voice. Their first attempts at reproduction were failures; the moment they sounded the voice, a powerful contraction

* Reproduced from "Voice, Song, and Speech."

of the muscles about the pharynx became visible, and the usual disagreeable effect was produced. By means of the mirror, I directed their attention to the constriction, and told them to expand the pharynx, as they had done before when they made no noise. At first they were unable to relax the muscles of the pharynx, without stopping the voice, but, after some practice, they succeeded in doing this, and at once the voice became natural and pleasant in quality.

The cavity of the pharynx may be roughly likened to a room with four walls. The back part ot the tongue constitutes the front wall of the chamber, and opposite to it is the back wall of the pharynx. The side walls are formed by muscles that extend upwards to the soft palate. The approximation of these side walls, as I have already explained, imparts to the voice a disagreeable metallic quality. The front and back walls, too, are capable of approximation, and in this case, also, the quality of the voice is injuriously affected. For example: The tongue may be held so far back in the mouth as to cause the base of the tongue to come almost into contact with the back of the pharynx. The voice then acquires a peculiar "guttural quality." I have heard this kind of voice produced by deaf children, but it is more common, I think, among persons who hear. It is rarely heard during the act of speech, but many persons affect this guttural quality of the voice when they sing. The "metallic quality" of voice, on the other hand, is quite common among the deaf, although it is rarely so marked as to be painful to the ear. Many hearing persons also possess it in a greater or less degree,—especially persons who use their voices much in the open air. For example, the rasping voice of the street hawker is of this description.

Another peculiarity of voice very common among the deaf, is "nasal quality." This is occasioned by the habitual depression of the soft palate. By means of a hand mirror, the cause may be shown to a deaf child.

The soft palate is capable of elevation and depression. When it is raised it fits closely against the back of the pharynx, forming a ceiling to the pharyngeal cavity. When it is depressed, it hangs down like a curtain, leaving a passage-way behind it, which leads into the nares or nasal passages.

I would recommend every teacher of articulation to learn to control the movements of the soft palate and the muscles of the pharynx, so as to be able to exhibit the action of the parts to pupils.

The first point you have to learn, is to depress the tongue so as to unveil the pharynx and soft palate. Many persons find difficulty in doing this, but by persistent efforts before a mirror, all can acquire the power. Now watch the soft palate while you breathe gently, sometimes through the mouth, sometimes through the nose. At first the soft palate appears to move about in a most mysterious manner by itself, without any volition on your part. Now it goes up, and then the next moment you see it hanging loosely down. By watching these motions in a mirror, and attempting to control them, you will soon find yourself able to elevate or depress the palate at will. Now sound the voice continuously, and observe what effect is produced upon its quality by the movement. You will notice that the moment the palate falls, the voice acquires nasality, and that this effect disappears when the palate is raised into contact with the back of the pharynx.

During the act of speech, the soft palate is raised continuously, excepting when the sound of *m*, *n*, and *ng*, are uttered. In order to correct a nasal quality of voice, therefore, your pupil must raise his soft palate. The question arises, however,—how are you going to make him do it?

Various expedients may be resorted to, such as the common one of telling him to blow an imaginary feather away from his mouth while he speaks; but these are all indirect methods, and do not touch the root of the matter. I would recommend you to go for the soft palate itself, directly, with a hand-mirror. Teach your pupil to elevate and depress it at will. Direct the action with your hand.

When you raise your hand let him raise the palate (Cut A), and keep it elevated till you give the signal for depression (Cut B).

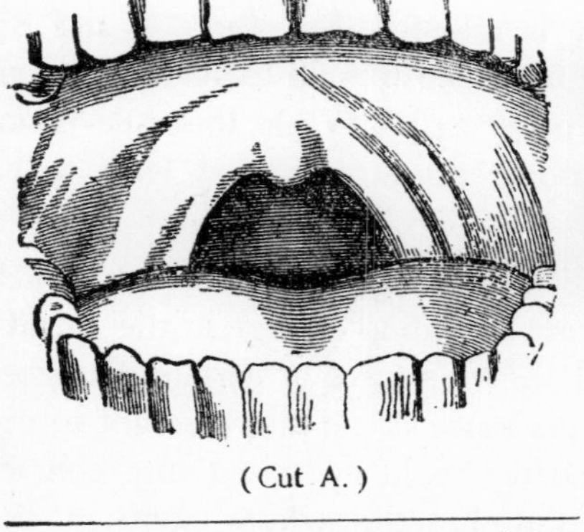

(Cut A.)

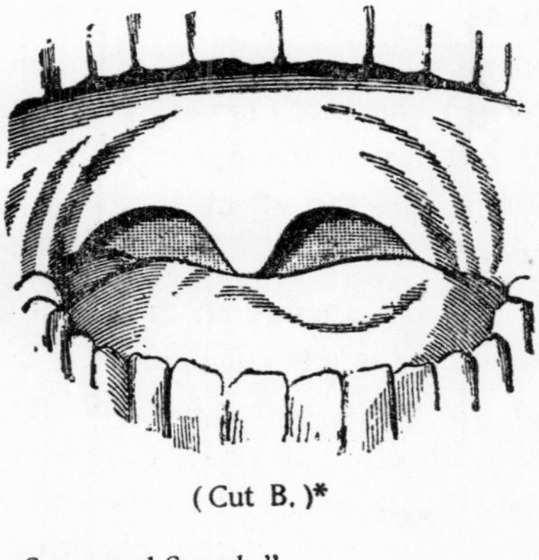

(Cut B.)*

* These cuts are reproduced from "Voice, Song, and Speech."

Then let him keep it depressed without motion, till you direct him to raise it. *Control over the vocal organs is gained not so much by moving them as by keeping them still.* Keep the soft palate depressed and *still* for a long period of time, and then raised for an equal length of time. Do this at first silently, and then afterwards with voice. Elevate and depress the palate without stopping the voice but retain the elevated or depressed position for a considerable period of time.

When your pupil can do this without looking in the mirror you may usefully vary the exercise by requiring him to raise or depress the palate while at the same time he prolongs a vowel sound. (For example: *ah* or *ee* or *o*.) Then let him rattle off a series of vowels without stopping the voice. (For example: *ah ee o ee; ah ee o ee,* etc.), elevating or depressing the palate as you direct. As the ultimate object to be gained is ability to retain the soft palate in the elevated position continuously during speech, there should be no rapid alternations of elevation and depression. He should repeat the series of vowels many times in succession with the soft palate raised, and many times with it depressed, but the voice should not be stopped excepting when it becomes advisable to take breath.

The uvula, the pendulous extremity of the soft palate, seems to have no special function in speech, at least in the English language, and I have known of cases where it has been excised without interfering with articulation. In teaching the deaf, however, the uvula may be found of use as an index to the pitch of the voice. A pupil may, perhaps, be made conscious of changes in the pitch of the voice, by directing his attention to changes that simultaneously occur in the length of the uvula. In most cases, the uvula hangs loosely down during the production of low tones and shrinks in size as the pitch of the voice is raised, (See Cuts A, and B.) When the pitch is very high the uvula shrinks up to such an extent that it almost disappears (Cut C, page 24.) While this rule is not invariable, the effect is so commonly produced, as at least to be worthy of note.

Every change in the shape of the passage-way, through which the voice is passed, occasions a corresponding change in the quality of the voice, and I have pointed out the causes of certain disagreeable effects. In order to render the voice sweet and pleasant to the ear, it is necessary that the soft palate should be raised into contact with the back of the pharynx, and that the whole cavity of the pharynx should be expanded, so that the passage-way there should be free and unobstructed. Any constriction in the pharynx is fatal to the beauty of the voice.

The mouth passage also affects the voice, imparting to it "vowel quality," and changes in the shape of the mouth-passage, produced by the action of the tongue and lips, occasion changes of vowel quality. In singing different vowel sounds the voice may have the same pitch and loudness, and yet each vowel remains distinct to the ear. Vowel differences, therefore, are differences in the quality or timbre of the voice; and vowels themselves are in reality *qualities of voice* to which we have given specific names, and which we employ as elements of speech.

I do not propose to-day to enter into any detailed description of the positions assumed by the tongue and lips, during the production of vowel sounds, as most of you, I know, are familiar with the

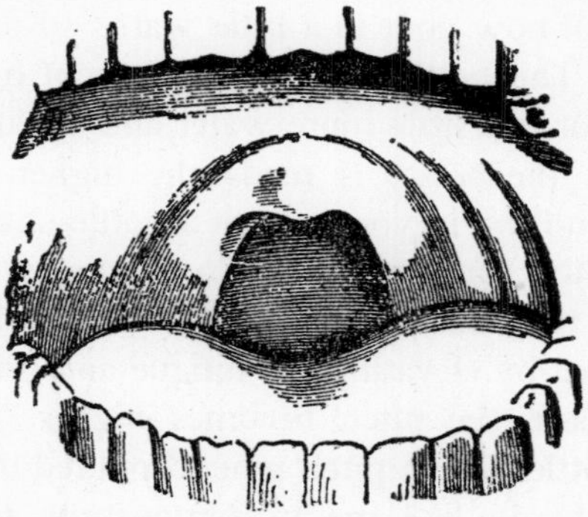

(Cut C).*

subject. I shall rather attempt to show you why it is that changes in the shape of the cavities of the mouth, pharynx, etc., occasion changes in the quality of the voice.

When we prolong a vowel sound without varying the pitch of the voice, the effect produced upon the ear is not simply that of a single musical sound, but of a chord containing a number of musical tones of different pitch. One of these tones is so much louder than the others that it determines the apparent pitch of the whole combination. The other tones are so feebly produced, that it takes a skilled ear to recognize them as musical effects at all; and the untrained ear simply perceives them as the quality or timbre of the sound. When a number of vowels are sung successively without varying the pitch of the voice, a trained ear readily perceives that

* This cut is reproduced from "Voice, Song, and Speech."

the partial tones change in pitch with every change of vowel effect. The loud fundamental is due to the vibration of the vocal cords, and the "partial tones" are caused by the resonance of the air in the cavities of the mouth.

"What do you mean by 'the resonance of the air in the cavities of the mouth?'" I fancy some of you ask. In order to answer this question I have brought a few empty bottles from the dining-room table and from the kitchen of the hotel. Here we have a pepper-pot, a pickle-bottle, a mustard-pot, a vinegar-bottle from the cruet-stand, and a few other bottles of different shapes and sizes. Now let me blow into the mouth of one of these bottles. At once you hear a musical tone something like that produced by an organ pipe. I shall now blow into the mouths of the others. You observe that each bottle has a resonance tone of its own. In some cases the pitch is high, in others low. Observe the pitch of the bottle I hold in my hand. I shall now pour in a little water so as to reduce the air space within. The bottle produces a tone of higher pitch than it did before. I pour in a little more water and again the pitch rises. In fact, the smaller the cavity is made the higher does the pitch become. Now you have in your mouth a bottle-shaped cavity, and in this case also the air within has a tendency to vibrate at a definite rate so as to produce a musical tone. When the size of the cavity is reduced by elevating the tongue and bringing it further forward in the mouth, the pitch becomes higher, just as the tone produced by the bottle rose in pitch when I poured in water. I am afraid you would hardly like me to demonstrate the truth of this statement by blowing into your mouth as I did into the bottle! If you are anxious to make the experiment you can blow into your own mouth with a pair of bellows! A still simpler way, however, of testing the effect is to blow air *through* the mouth from the lungs. For example: whistle. The pitch of the whistle rises as the tongue is advanced in the mouth.

Let me direct your attention once more to the bottle. The pitch rose when I poured in water, and of course I can lower it again, if I choose, by pouring out the water. Instead of doing this, however, I shall change the pitch in another way, without varying the size of the air space within. While I blow into the bottle I shall gradually cover its mouth with my hand. The tone, you observe, falls in pitch as the orifice is reduced. You see from this that you can vary the pitch; (1) by varying the size of the cavity, and (2) by changing the size of the opening into it. Allow me to illustrate these two ways with my mouth.

1. I shall assume the position of the Visible Speech symbol "Back center-aperture" (German *ch* in the word *nach*); and then glide the tongue gradually forward to the position for "Front centre-aperture" (*h* in the word *hue*) thus reducing the size of the cavity in front of the tongue. The pitch of the sound rises as the tongue is advanced in the mouth.

2. I shall now retain tne "Back centre-aperture position (German *ch*) and gradually contract the aperture between the lips until the position fcr the English element *wh* is reached. The pitch falls as the labial aperture is reduced.

In forming German *ch* compressed air from the lungs escapes through a very small aperture between the back of the tongue and the soft palate, occasioning a rustling sound in the mouth. Although this effect constitutes a noise rather than a musical tone, you have no difficulty in recognizing that it has pitch.

I think you should teach all your pupils to produce German *ch*, because this position of the tongue enters into the composition of three English elements which are usually pronounced in a very defective manner. I allude to the sounds of *wh*, *w*, and the vowei *oo* in the word *too*. In these cases the aperture between the lips is so small as to prevent the pupil from observing the position of the tongue, which position is essential to the production of the sound. He imitates the labial aperture perfectly, but fails to give the back tongue position, and hence produces only a crude approximation to the correct sound.

A short time ago I visited one of our best articulation schools, and went through all the classes in search of a good *oo*. The only children who gave the sound correctly were semi-deaf, or had acquired speech by ear. There is really little difficulty in teaching the sound if you commence with the lingual element by itself, and then modify it by rounding the lips. Commence with German *ch*. Round the lips and you have *wh*. Add voice and you have *oo*. For all practical purposes this may be considered identical with *w*. When the two elements are in juxtaposition the difference is readily perceived by the pupil. For example: Pronounce the word *woo*. The labial aperture is visibly smaller for the consonant than for the vowel. The only trouble in teaching this sound arises from the fact that a very slight change in the lingual position destroys the *oo* effect. If the tongue is only a little too far forward or a little too far back, the position may yield a very respectable German *ch*, and yet fail to produce a good *oo* when the lips are rounded and the voice is sounded. In such cases the pitch of the German *ch* will tell you the nature of the defect, and how to remedy it. If the pitch is too high the tongue is too far forward; if it is too low the tongue is too far back. You can obtain your standard for comparison in the following way: Pronounce a good *oo*. Convert it into *wh* by substituting breath for voice, and then force your lips apart so as to obtain the effect of the lingual position alone. Observe the pitch of the German *ch* thus produced. If the pitch of the sound produced by your pupil is higher than this, direct him to place the tongue further back; and if it is lower, tell him to bring the tongue forward.

The pitch of the mouth can be brought out by other means than by blowing air into or through the cavity. Resonance is caused whenever a sound of similar pitch is produced in the neighborhood. For example: Here is a tuning fork, and upon the table is a bottle which has the same pitch. I hold the vibrating prongs of the fork over the mouth of the bottle, and at once its resonance tone is loudly evoked. Here is another bottle, but it remains silent when the fork is applied. Upon blowing into it you perceive that the pitch is too low. Let me tune it by pouring in water. It still fails to respond—the pitch is now too high. Upon pouring out a little water the bottle resounds, but very faintly. It has almost the same pitch as the fork—but is still a little too high. I pour out a few more drops, and now you hear the full and loud response made when the fork is applied. Let me hold the fork in front of my lips while my mouth is in the position of *wh*. You have no response, because the proper tone of the mouth cavity is different from that of the fork. Upon tuning the cavity by shifting the position of the tongue, the mouth resounds as the bottle did a few moments ago.

In these cases you have resonance produced by "sympathetic vibration." If you have in the same neighborhood two bodies that tend to vibrate at the same rate, set the one vibrating and the other vibrates of itself—out of "sympathy" as it were! I shall show you another case. Here we have a piano. I shall depress the pedal so as to release all the strings, and then sing into the instrument. When I stop singing you will observe that the piano echoes my voice. That string of the piano that had the same pitch as my voice was set sympathetically into vibration. A similar effect is produced in the case of vibrations which are too slow to produce the sensation of sound. For example: If two clocks having pendulums of similar length are attached to the same wall you need only set one of them going, for by and by the other will go by itself. Of course we cannot suppose that the pendulums had any particular "sympathy" or affection one for the other—or that the string of the piano experienced any emotion at the sound of my voice! Every mechanical effect must have a mechanical cause—and the facts of "sympathetic vibration" require explanation. Let us consider the case of an oscillation slow enough to be followed by the eye. For example: Imagine one of your pupils to be upon a swing. Stand behind him and give him a shove. The swing moves forward a little way and returns upon its path. It oscillates backwards and forwards at a definite rate for a long time before it comes to rest. Indeed, were it not for friction and resistance of the air it wouldn't stop at all. Inertia would keep it going; and one shove would be sufficient to set it vibrating forever! In spite of the resistance of air, the effect of a single push is retained through many vibrations. If, then, you push the swing again at the proper time, the motion is increased. Very slight efforts of the hand will suffice to set the swing into full vibration if the impulses are properly timed to the movements of the swing so as always to come during the forward motion alone. Under such circumstances the effect of each successive shove is added to that of the last, and a cumulative effect is produced. The amplitude may become very great even though the individual impulses are slight. If the shove is given at the wrong time, that is, when the swing is moving on its backward path, then every impulse tends to stop the vibration. Each push retards the motion to a certain extent, and a series of very slight impulses will bring the swing to rest. For example: The resistance of the air stops it in time if you leave it alone. The air, in effect, shoves the swing at the wrong time at each vibration. Make it push *at the right time,* and the converse effect will be produced. You could set the swing going, for instance, by puffs from a pair of bellows!

Now the strings of a piano are in effect swings, each tuned to vibrate at a different rate from the other; and puffs of air from my lungs set them going when I sang into the instrument. At each opening of the glottis a puff of air escaped from the lungs, and all the strings of the piano received a shove. The first shove started them all swinging, but the second caught some of them on the return path and stopped their motion. The motion of others was retarded later on; but that string which had the same rate of vibration as my vocal cords, received each shove always at the right time, and was thus set into vigorous vibration. It continued sounding for some time after I stopped the voice, just as a swing continues in vibration after you stop pushing it. The same kind of action took place when the tuning fork was held over a bottle of similar pitch to its own. At each descent of the prong the air in the bottle received a shove; and the air was thus set into vibration, as you set a swing into vibration by the hand.

A similar action took place when I held the vibrating fork in front of my lips. At first no sound was produced, but when I shifted the position of the tongue, so as to tune the mouth-cavity to the pitch of the fork, resonance resulted, and you all heard the effect. I have no doubt that the Scotchman with the artificial larynx could have produced the same effect, if he had slipped a tuning-fork into his throat in place of the harmonium reed. Imagine a multitude of tuning-forks of different pitch to be massed together in front of the mouth and all simultaneously to be set in vibration. It should then be possible, by shifting the position of the tongue, to reinforce the tone—now of one fork, now of another—at will. Indeed under such circumstances, it would hardly be possible to assume a position of the mouth, that would *not* reinforce some fork—at least in a greater or less degree. Imagine the mass of tuning-forks to be placed in the Scotchman's throat, and similar effects would result.

Now the vocal cords like the hypothetical forks, produce a number of feeble tones of different pitch; when we pronounce a vowel sound, the mouth cavity reinforces, by resonance, that "partial tone" of the voice which is nearest in pitch, to the proper tone of the cavity. The effect produced we call the "vowel quality." The loud fundamental tone of the voice, so distracts the attention of the untrained observer, that he finds difficulty at first in hearing the resonance tone produced by the mouth. The best way to train the ear is to commence by observing the pitches of non-vocal sounds. Then listen for similar effects when the voice is sounded.

If you whisper the vowels ***ah, aw, ōh, ōō,*** I think you will have little difficulty in recognizing the fact that the pitch of the whisper falls as the lips are approximated. More difficulty will be experienced in determining the relative pitches of other vowels. For example: whisper the vowels in the words *eel, ill, ale, ell* and ***shall.*** The pitch changes with each vowel, but how does it change? I attempted to determine the point a good many years ago, and came to the conclusion that the vowels formed a descending musical scale, *ee* having the highest, and *ă* the lowest pitch. To my surprise, however, my father was unable to agree with me in this result. To his ear, the vowels formed an ascending series, *ee* having the lowest, and *ă* the highest pitch. The fact is, we were both right, for these vowels have a double resonance. The passage-way for the voice extends from the vocal cords to the lips, and if you constrict it at any point, you divide it into two parts forming bottle-shaped cavities placed neck to neck. (See diagram, Fig. 3.) There is a cavity in front of the point of constriction and another behind it.

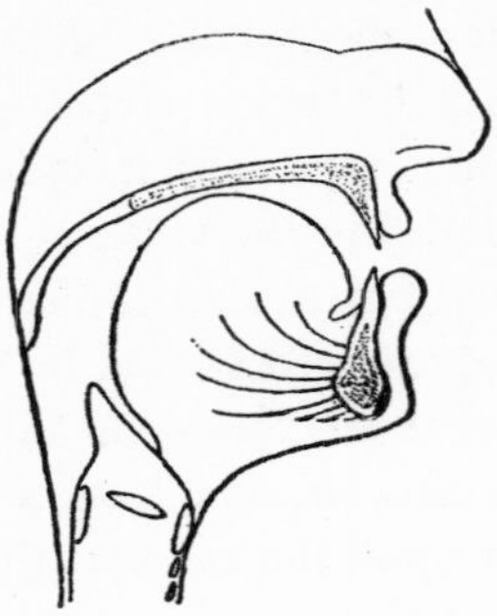

Fig 3.

In forming *ee*, the front cavity is very small, and the pitch consequently high; but the back cavity is low in pitch, because it possesses an extremely narrow neck at the point of constriction. In pronouncing the other vowels of the series mentioned, the front cavity increases in size, and, therefore, falls in pitch; but the pitch of the back cavtiy rises because the neck at the point of constriction is enlarged. I can demonstrate the double resonance of these vowels by a simple experiment. I shall hold the side of a lead pencil against my cheek, and tap it forcibly with my thumb nail, so as to agitate the air in the front cavity, while I whisper the vowels *ee, ĭ, ā, ĕ, ă*. You perceive at once a descending series of sounds, in which *ee* is the highest, and *ă* the lowest pitch. I shall now hold the pencil against my throat so that each tap may agitate the air in the back cavity. Upon whispering the same vowels, the taps produce an ascending series, *ee* having the lowest pitch and *ă* the highest. The effect is improved by closing the glottis so as to convert the back cavity into a bottle closed at the bottom. The front cavity also yields a much louder effect if it is shut off completely from the back cavity, by allowing the soft palate to fall into contact with the back of the tongue (*ng* position). In these cases, of course, the vowel positions must be silently assumed. When we pronounce these vowels aloud, feeble "partial tones," due to the resonance of the air in the back and front cavities of the mouth, mingle with the tone of the voice, and produce in our ears the sensation of "vowel quality."

Helmholtz has not only resolved vowels, by a process of analysis, into their constituent musical elements, but has produced vowel sounds artificially by a synthetical process. In place of voice, he caused a tuning fork to vibrate continuously in front of a tuned bottle or "resonator," thus producing a loud musical tone. He then selected two forks having the pitches of the partial tones he had recognized as characteristic of the vowel *ee*. One was very high, and the other low. (They represented, indeed, the front and back cavities of the mouth in forming the vowel.) These forks were then placed in front of bottles, tuned almost but not quite to their own pitch, so that the sounds produced should be very faint. The simultaneous vibration of the three forks in front of their respective resonators, or bottles, produced one loud sound, and two feeble partial tones. The effect upon the ear was that of the vowel *ee*.

Those of you who desire to pursue this subject further, may consult a paper of mine upon "Vowel Theories," which was read before the National Academy of Sciences, April 15, 1879, and was published in the *Journal of Otology,* Vol. 1, July, 1879. This paper is printed as an Appendix in this volume.

Dr. Bell: Prof. Gordon has received a communication from Prof. Samuel Porter of Gallaudet College, Washington, D. C., a gentleman who knows about as much about the mechanism of speech as any man living. I am sure that we all regret Prof. Porter's absence from this meeting, and shall be glad to hear Prof. Gordon read the communication which he will now do:

Farmington, Conn., June 30, 1891.

My Dear Friend: I notice that Dr. Bell is to lecture on the Functions of the Pharynx in Speech. I should like to know what he would have to say about that. My idea is, that it is quite common to misapprehend by regarding the pharynx too much as if absolutely separated from the mouth. In fact, when the soft palate is raised in non-nasal utterance, the pharynx and the mouth are better regarded as together forming a single cavity. There is no line of separation across the tongue, and nothing whatever as a line of demarcation, except the posterior pillars of the fauces, which in each case almost lose themselves in the walls of the passage. The pharynx comes into importance, if we regard, as I do, the *a* (*ah*) vowel as made with the place of constriction against the back wall of the pharynx, thus giving this vowel a place to the rear of the proper "back vowels," *aw*, *o*, *oo*, etc., which have the place of constriction in the soft palate. Bell might symbolize it by an additional turn ( ). This relieves Bell and Sweet from the vacillation and diversity in the place assigned by them to this vowel. The pharynx acts together with the cheeks and the soft palate in producing, by their elastic reaction, the explosion of a *p*, and, without the cheeks, of a *t*, and, by itself alone, of a *k*. I imagine also that the pharynx acts, together with the soft palate, as a cushion, and may thus be made to affect the ring of the voice or quality of tone, giving it sometimes softness, and sometimes sonority in the "orotund" quality, etc.

Yours truly,

(Signed) Samuel Porter.

THE FUNCTIONS OF THE EPIGLOTTIS AND SOFT PALATE.

The instrument of speech consists essentially of a collection of tubes or passage-ways connected together somewhat as shown in the following crude diagram, which I have found of assistance in explaining to pupils the functions of the epiglottis and soft palate. (See Fig. 4.)

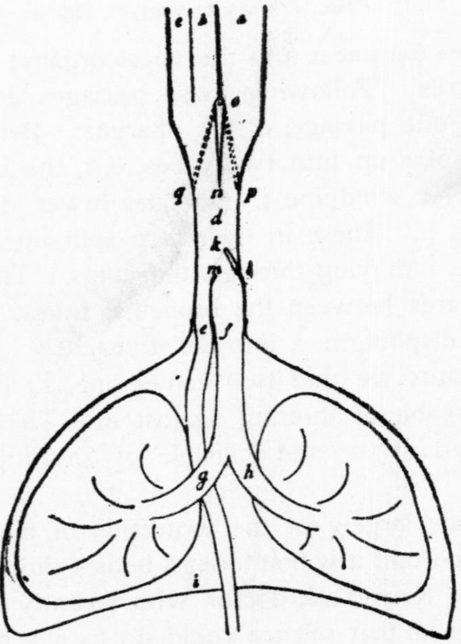

Fig. 4.
Diagram illustrating the action of the epiglottis (k) and soft palate (n).

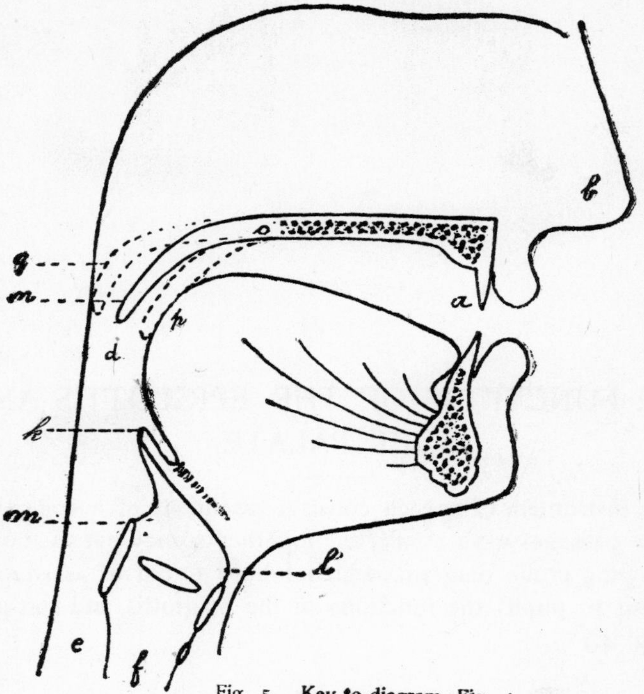

Fig. 5. **Key to diagram, Fig. 4.**

There are three entrances into the vocal organs; a, the mouth, and b, c, the nostrils. Following these passages downwards we find they unite in one passage, d, the pharynx. Below this point the passage-way splits up into two tubes, e, f, the æsophagus and the windpipe. The windpipe, f, bifurcates lower down into the bronchial tubes, g, h. These in their turn split up into multitudinous smaller tubes, ramifying through the lungs. The æsophagus, e, passes downwards between the bronchial tubes, g, h, through an aperture in the diaphragm, i, into the stomach.

In this apparatus we find two valves one, k, (the epiglottis) hinged at l, and capable of shutting against m. The other, n, (the soft palate), hinged at o, and capable of shutting against p, and q.

These valves are largely for the protection of the lungs. We all know how important it is that foreign bodies should be kept out of the lungs. The New York doctor who recently inhaled a cork has died, in spite of all that science could do to aid him. Equally serious results might follow were particles of food to find their way into the lungs.

The pharynx, d, forms a common passage-way through which both food and air pass, and the valves, k, n, prevent the passage of food into the wind-pipe, and permit breathing to take place with safety during the process of mastication. If we were obliged to breathe through the mouth-passage, a, while the mouth contains partly masticated food, it would be almost impossible to prevent particles from being drawn into the lungs with the breath. The valve, n (the soft palate), obviates such a catastrophe by shutting in the contents of the mouth during the process of mastication, by closing against p (the back of the tongue), as shown by dotted lines. Breathing can be carried on safely behind the soft palate through the nasal passages, b, c. When, however, the process of mastication is completed, a new danger threatens the lungs. The food, on its way to the stomach through the æsophagus, e, must pass the upper end of the wind-pipe, f. The valve, k, (the epiglottis), closes tightly against m during the act of swallowing, and thus prevents the possibility of food obtaining access to the wrong passage-way. The larynx constitutes a sort of box on top of the wind-pipe, of which the epiglottis k, forms the lid. In the diagram, I have represented the lid as shutting down on the top of the box, but in the actual instrument of speech the box also shuts up against the lid. Place your hand against your throat, and you can feel the larynx rise when you make the act of swallowing. In speech, the soft palate, n, is used for the purpose of directing the breath through the mouth or nasal passages, as desired, When it shuts against p, (the back of the tongue), air from the lungs passes up behind it through the nasal passages, b, c, and no air can escape through the mouth, a. When it shuts against q, (the back of the pharynx), air from the lungs passes in front of it, through the mouth, a, and no air escapes through the nasal passages, b, c. When it hangs half way down, as shown in the position o, n, air from the lungs escapes through all three passages, a, b, c, simultaneously

METHODS OF STUDYING THE MECHANISM OF SPEECH.

I have already directed your attention to the fact that many words, and even sentences, may be pronounced during a single effort of expiration. The muscles concerned in expiration produce a continuous, steady pressure upon the air in the thorax, during the act of speech. In fact, we play upon the instrument of speech as the piper plays upon the bagpipe. The piper's arm continuously squeezes the bag all the time he is playing. He does not jerk his arm in time to the music. A continuous, steady pressure exists all the time his fingers are moving. When an amateur tries to play upon the bagpipe for the first time, he is apt to give a fresh squeeze for every note, producing an effect somewhat like the jerky utterance of deaf children who have been taught word-by-word articulation.

When children are taught at first to pronounce each word by itself, with a distinct and separate effort of emission, an intermittent action of the abdominal muscles is apt to become habitual, even in rapid utterance.

We have had the opportunity of listening to pupils from Milwaukee, Boston, and Philadelphia, and I have been delighted to observe that they do not exhibit this fault. Whatever defects of speech they possess, they do not exhibit the fundamental error of word-by-word, syllable-by-syllable articulation. I would certainly recommend to your notice the exercises that have been so successful in producing continuity of utterance in their cases.

The material from which speech is made, is a store of compressed air within the thorax, which is let out little by little, in a continuous, steady stream, and moulded into the various sounds of speech. No compression is possible unless the escape of air is restrained. In order that we should have a continuous, steady stream, it is necessary that emission should take place through only a very fine orifice. You all probably know the effect of restraining the emission of fluid from a pipe, under pressure. If you haven't made the experiment, partially plug the orifice of a faucet with your finger, while the water is running. At once the slow, silent stream, is converted into a rushing torrent, which spurts out with great noise. Instead of a large quantity of water coming out slowly, you have a small quantity rushing out quickly. Instead of a silent flow you have noise. In the production of noise a little water goes a great way, and a steady stream can be sustained for a long period of time, without the expenditure of much fluid.

In a similar manner, noise is produced by partially plugging the air-passage from the lungs; and all the elements of speech result from constrictions of some kind. In studying the mechanism of speech-sounds, therefore, it is necessary to determine the location and nature of those constrictions that produce and modify the sounds.

Now how are you going to describe a constriction? My father has pointed out that the principal organs concerned in the production of speech, naturally group themselves into two classes, active and passive. As a general rule, the lower organs are active, and the upper passive. For example: In forming the sound of *t*, the point of the tongue is the active agent involved, and the upper gum is the passive. In this case the two organs are approximated together in such a manner as to completely close the passage-way between them.

In describing other constrictions also, it is usual to designate:—

(*a*) The active organ employed;
(*b*) The passive organ; and
(*c*) The condition of the passage-way between them.

Whether or not we adopt my father's classification into active and passive organs, it is certainly the case that we are obliged, in defining accurately the location and nature of a constriction, to distinguish three associated elements, viz:—

{*a*, *b*} Two organs which are approximated together; and
(*c*) The condition of the passage-way between them.

A constriction is usually termed "a position of the vocal organs." When two or more positions of the vocal organs are simultaneously assumed, the effect upon the ear is that of a single sound. In such a case the passage-way is constricted at more than one point at the same time. For example: Take the vowel *oo*, in such a word as *too*. In forming this sound three distinct positions (P, P′, P″,) are simultaneously assumed. (See Fig. 6.)

P. A labial position.

The two organs?	a	The under lip.
	b	The upper lip.
Passage-way between?	c	A small central aperture.

P′. A lingual position.

The two organs?	a′	The back of the tongue.
	b′	The soft palate.
Passage-way between?	c′	A small central aperture.

P″. A laryngeal position.

The two organs?	a″, b″	The two vocal cords.
Passage-way between?	c″	A slit-like aperture.

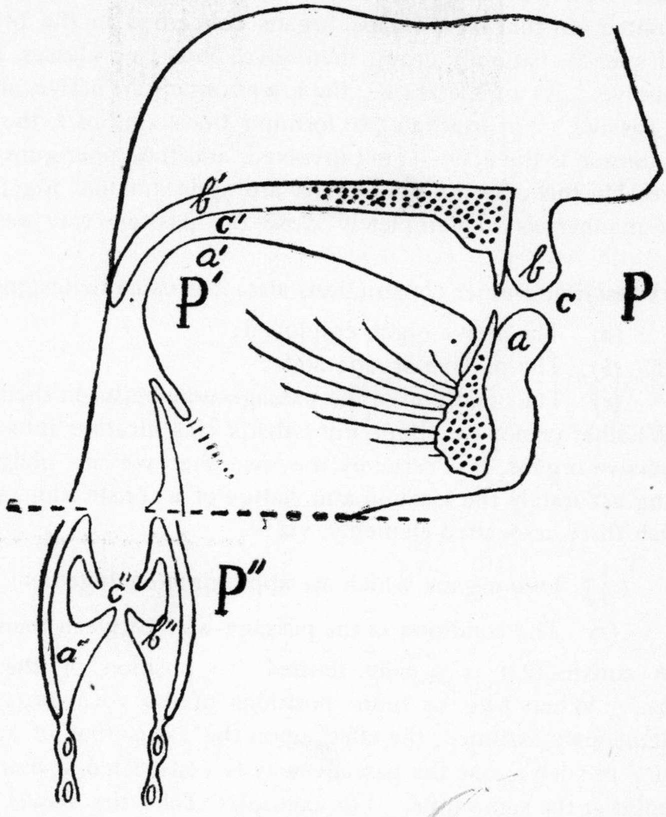

Fig. 6. Positions of the vocal organs in forming the vowel $\overline{oo}$ in "too." In this diagram a side view of the mouth is given in section, but a front view of the larynx so as to show both of the vocal cords.

The last position (P″) represents the condition of the glottis in forming "voice." The passage of air through the slit-like aperture occasions a vibration of the vocal cords. The glottis then alternately opens and closes with great rapidity, causing the emission of a series of puffs from the lungs. These puffs follow each other with such rapidity that the ear fails to distinguish the individual impulses, and recognizes only a continuous effect of a musical character, which we term "voice."

When we come to study the method of symbolizing positions of the vocal organs devised by my father, Prof. A. Melville Bell, and called by him "Visible Speech," we shall find great advantage from considering the symbols as algebraical signs. Positions, (like P, P′, and P″), which are simultaneously assumed, may be considered as added together ($P+P'+P''$); but the three elements (a b c) which compose each position, must be taken as multiplied into one another ($a\times b\times c$.) Thus:—

Position for *oo*= $P+P'+P''=a\ b\ c + a'\ b'\ c' + a''\ b''\ c''$.

Position symbols placed in juxtaposition without any connective sign between them must be taken as successively, not simultaneously, assumed. Thus $P\ P'\ P''$ means: Assume first the position P alone, then P' alone, and then P'' alone.

If the positions (P, P', P'',) are assumed separately, instead of together, they yield sounds that are quite unlike the vowel *oo*. For example: If the labial position (P) be assumed without any other constriction in the passage-way, a sound results which is not an English element of speech. English-speaking children, however, give the sound when they blow upon their porridge to make it cool.

If the lingual position (P') alone be assumed, the resulting sound is the German *ch* in such a word as *nach*.

If the vocalizing position of the glottis, (P''), be assumed without any other constriction higher up in the passage-way, an indefinite vowel sound results like the *er-er-er* of a hesitating speaker, or like the vowel heard in such words as *her*, *sir*, *word*, etc.

If two of the positions (P, P', P'',) are simultaneously assumed without the third, still other sounds result which neither resemble the vowel *oo*, nor the sounds I have just described. For example:

If the positions P and P' are simultaneously assumed without P'', the English consonant *wh* is produced.

If the positions P and P'' are simultaneously assumed without P', the sound heard is that of the German *w*, in the word *wie*.

If the positions P' and P'' are simultaneously assumed without P, the result is the Gaelic vowel in the word "*laogh*."

These facts may be arranged in tabular form as follows:

POSITIONS ASSUMED.	RESULTING SOUNDS.
P	Blowing to cool.
P'	German *ch* in "*nach*."
P''	The vowel *er* in "*her*."
$P+P'$	The consonant *wh* in "*what*."
$P+P''$	German *w* in "*wie*."
$P'+P''$	Gaelic "*aohg*" in "*laogh*."
$P+P'+P''$	The vowel *oo* in "*too*."

What we term an "element of speech" may in reality, like the vowel *oo*, be the result of a combination of positions. The true element of articulation, I think, is a constriction or position of the vocal organs rather than a sound. Combinations of positions yield new sounds just as combinations of chemical elements yield new substances. Water is a substance of very different character from either of the gases of which it is formed; and the vowel *oo* is a sound of very different character from that of any of its elementary positions.

When we symbolize positions, the organic relations of speech-sounds to one another can be shown by means of an equation, for example:—

English *wh* $= P + P'$.
German *ch* $= P'$.
Hence German *ch* = English *wh* $- P$.

The equation asserts that the English *wh* without the labial constriction (P) is the German *ch*.

I performed this equation upon the mouth of Mr. Lyon during the course of my last lecture. While Mr. Lyon was prolonging the sound of *wh*, I forced his lips apart with my fingers, and you then heard the sound of German *ch*. Take another case:—

The English vowel *oo* in "too" $= P + P' + P''$.
The Gaelic vowel "*aogh*" in "*laogh*" $= P' + P''$.
Hence "*aogh*" = *oo* $- P$.

That is: The English vowel "*oo*," without the labial constriction (P) is *the Gaelic vowel "aogh.*"

If then you desire to pronounce the Gaelic vowel "*aogh,* "sing the vowel *oo* while some one else forces your lips apart. This is a direction that will enable any English-speaking person to convert the known vowel *oo* into the unknown Gaelic sound "*aogh,*" without the aid of hearing. In a similar manner, the sounds known to the deaf child can be converted into the unknown sounds of the English language. Indeed, manipulation succeeds better with a deaf person than with one who hears, because the hearing person attempts to retain the *sound,* whereas the deaf child simply tries to retain the *position.*

The symbols of Visible Speech bear the same relation to phonetics that chemical symbols do to the science of chemistry. In dealing with the mechanism of speech, it is as necessary now-a-days to make use of my father's symbols, as it is to use chemical symbols in treating of the composition of matter.

As many of you are already familiar with the subject, it will not be necessary for me to enter into any detailed description of Visible Speech. I shall, therefore, to-day, simply attempt to give a general idea of the nature of my father's method of symbolizing positions of the vocal organs, so as to enable those who are unfamiliar with the subject to follow me intelligently in my use of the symbols.

The fundamental characters represent the vocal organs and the various kinds of apertures employed in the production of speech; and these can be combined into a compound form to express a position of the vocal organs.

A character shaped like a tube (⊂) is used to denote a very small aperture for the escape of breath; and when this tube is plugged up at one end (⊐) the symbol then indicates complete closure of the passage-way.

The symbols for the principal organs of speech are shown in Figure 7.

The active organs of the mouth, viz: the under lip, the point of the tongue, the top or "front" part of the tongue, and the back of the tongue are represented by curves that form, in such a diagram as that shown, the outlines of the organs themselves. This pictorial basis forms an element of great value in teaching the deaf.

The upper or "passive" organs, to which the lower or "active" organs are usually applied, are represented by the same symbols, written upon a small scale.

Thus, the symbol for the upper lip is a miniature of that for the lower lip; the upper gum, to which the point of the tongue is usually applied, has the point-tongue sign upon a small scale; the top of the hard palate is expressed by the symbol for the top or "front" of the tongue; and that part of the soft palate to which the back of the tongue is applied, is denoted by the back-tongue symbol upon a reduced scale.

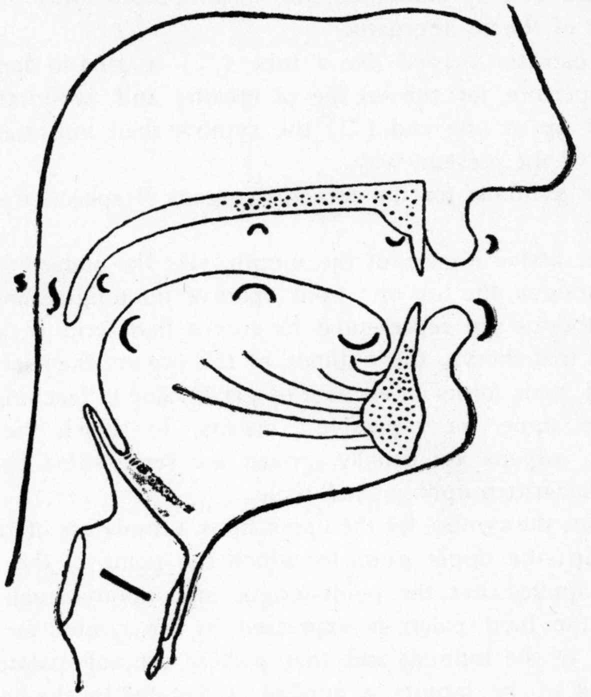

Fig 7.

) **Under lip.**	ɔ Upper lip.
⌣ Point of tongue.	ᴗ Upper gum.
⌢ " Top " or " Front " **part of tongue.**	∩ Top of hard **palate.**
(Back of tongue.	c Front part of soft **palate.**
ʃ Back of soft palate.	ʾ Back of pharynx **behind soft palate.**
| **Slit-like aperture between the vocal cords.**	

The mode of combining these characters so as to express a position of the vocal organs, may be illustrated by symbolizing the constrictions shown in diagram Fig. 6.

	Expressed upon plan shown in Fig. 6.	Definition.	Expressed upon plan shown in Fig. 7.
The Labial Position	P		$Ɔ^{ɔ}$
The two organs	a	The under lip	)
	b	The upper lip	ɔ
Passage-way between ?	c	A small central aperture	⊂
	P = a b c		$Ɔ^{ɔ}$ = ⊂$Ɔ^{ɔ}$
The Lingual Position	P′		C^{c}
The two organs ?	a′	The back of the tongue	(
	b′	The soft palate	c
Passage-way between ?	c′	A small central aperture	⊂
	P′ = a′ b′ c′		C^{c} = ⊂C^{c}
The Laryngeal Position	P″		I
The two organs ?	a″, b″	The two vocal cords	These are implied and are not specially symbolized.
Passage-way between ?	c″	A slit-like aperture	I
	P″ = a″ b″ c″		I = A slit-like aperture between the vocal cords.

The various combinations of these positions tabulated upon page 42, may be symbolized as follows:

POSITIONS ASSUMED.

Expressed upon plan shown in Fig. 6.	Expressed upon plan shown in Fig. 7.	RESULTING SOUNDS.
P	Ɔ^{ɔ}	Blowing to cool.
P′	C^{c}	German *ch* in "*nach.*"
P″	I	The vowel *er* in "*her.*"
P + P′	Ɔ^{ɔ} + C^{c}	The consonant *wh* in "*what.*"
P + P″	Ɔ^{ɔ} + I	German *w* in "*wie.*"
P′ + P″	C^{c} + I	Gaelic *aogh* in "*laogh.*"
P + P′ + P″	Ɔ^{ɔ} + C^{c} + I	The vowel *oo* in "*too.*"

The equations to which I have directed your attention may be thus expressed:

1. German *ch* = English *wh* — P.

C^{c} = (Ɔ^{ɔ} + C^{c}) — Ɔ^{ɔ}

2. Gaelic *aogh* = English *oo* — P.

C^{c} + I = (Ɔ^{ɔ} + C^{c} + I) — Ɔ^{ɔ}

Three positions (P, P′, P″), have been shown in Fig. 6, but a fourth position, which has not hitherto been noticed, is also indicated in that diagram.

The soft palate is in contact with the back of the pharynx, thus closing the entrance to the nasal passages. Visible Speech affords us a means of expressing this position if we so desire. The portion of the soft palate that fits against the back of the pharynx, like other active organs, is represented by its own outline (ʃ), in such a diagram as Fig. 7; and the part of the pharynx with which it makes contact could, consistently with the notation, be represented by the same symbol in miniature (').

Combining these with the symbol for passage-way closed (⊐), we could form the compound character ⊐' (soft palate shut against back of pharynx). In English utterance this position is constantly assumed during the act of speech, excepting when the sounds of *m, n,* and *ng* occur. As a matter of convenience the position of the soft palate is not noted excepting when these sounds occur.

When the soft palate is depressed, as in Fig. 7, a passage-way exists between it and the back of the pharynx, through which air escapes into the nasal passages.

This position may be thus expressed:

Ɛ' { "A central aperture between the soft palate and the back of the pharynx."

In forming *m* we shut the lips and pass voice through the nose. This sound, therefore, results from three positions which are simultaneously assumed.

Position for *m* = D᷾ + Ɛ' + I (See Fig. 8).

That is: "Under lip shut against upper lip" plus "central aperture, between the soft palate and back of the pharynx," plus "slit-like aperture between the vocal cords."

Position for *n* = Ʊᵘ + Ɛ' + I (See Fig. 9).

That is, "point of tongue, shut against upper gum" plus "central aperture, between the soft palate, and back of the pharynx,' plus "slit-like aperture between the vocal cords."

Position for *ng* = Ɑᶜ + Ɛ' + I (See Fig. 10).

That is: "Back of the tongue shut against the soft palate" plus "central aperture, between the soft palate and back of the pharynx" plus "slit-like aperture between the vocal cords."

RESUMÉ OF ELEMENTARY POSITIONS.

D᷾ = Under lip, shut against upper lip.

Ʊᵘ = Point of tongue, shut against upper gum.

Ωⁿ = Top (or "front") of tongue, shut, against top of hard palate.

Ɑᶜ = Back of tongue, shut against soft palate.

Ɒ' = Soft palate, shut against back of pharynx.

Ɔ᷾ = Central aperture, between the under lip and the upper lip.

Ʊᵘ = Central aperture between the point of the tongue and the upper gum.

∩ⁿ = Central aperture between the top (or "front") of the tongue and the hard palate.

Cᶜ = Central aperture between the back of the tongue and the soft palate.

Ɛ' = Central aperture between the soft palate and back of the pharynx.

I = Slit-like aperture between the two vocal cords.

An elementary position is expressed by a symbol composed of three associated characters. For example:—

Ɔ᷾ = Ɔ᷾ or P = a b c. (Fig. 6).

The sign for the constriction (c) is united with that for the

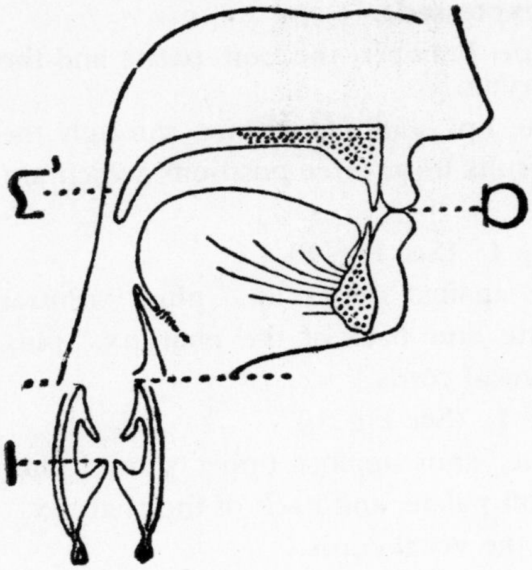

Fig. 8. Position for **M.**

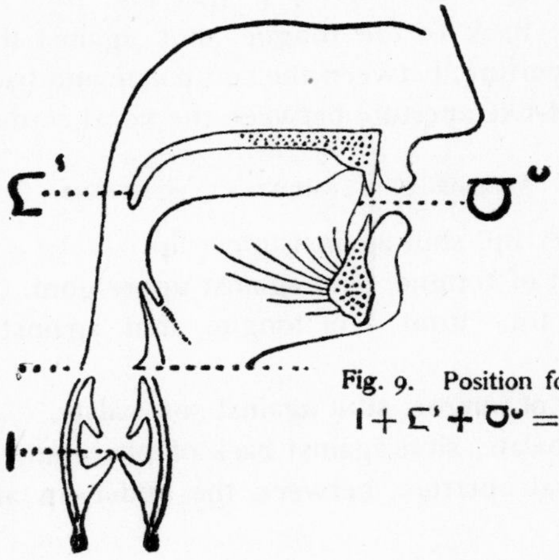

Fig. 9. Position for N.

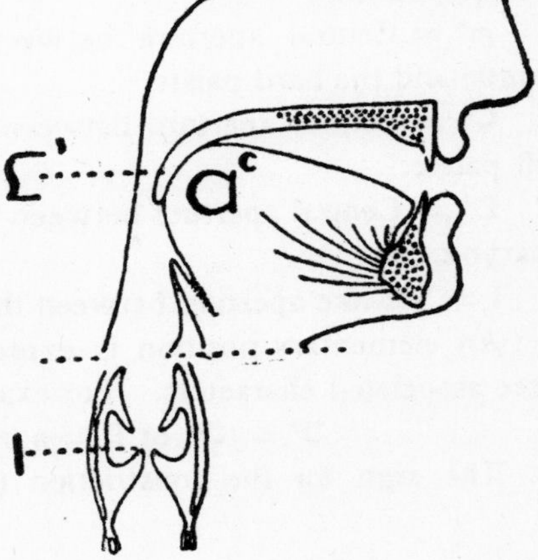

Fig. 10. Position for NG.

active organ (a) so as to form one character; and the passive organ (b) appears as a diacritical mark.

In order to express the mechanism of speech-sounds with accuracy, as many symbols are required as there are elementary positions to be represented. Hence many sounds like the vowel *oo* (Fig. 6), require at least three position-symbols to express their formation. (See also positions for *m*, *n*, and *ng;* Figs. 8, 9, 10.)

This method of symbolization, though admirable for the purposes of scientific analysis, would be unsuitable for current use as a phonetical representation of speech. For example: It would hardly be convenient to write the word "moon" in the following way!

M	*OO*	*N*
(Ɒ° + Ⲉ' + I)	(Ɔ° + Cᶜ + I)	Ʊᵘ + Ⲉ' + I)
See Fig. 8.	See Fig. 6	See Fig. 9.

In order to fit the symbols for use as a phonetical alphabet, my father saw that it was necessary, or at all events advisable, that each sound should be represented by only one character; and that therefore, associated positions should be combined into a compound form capable of use like a letter of the alphabet.

By the adoption of certain principles of abbreviation this has been accomplished without interfering with the symbolic character of the notation.

ABBREVIATIONS.

1. Passive organs may in general be implied and not written. This plan gets rid of the diacritical marks save in exceptional cases. For example: Ʊ ("Point shut") alone, without any representation of the passive organ, is to be taken as meaning Ʊᵘ ("Point shut against the upper gum") for the upper gum is the usual place of application for the point of the tongue. The symbol expresses the position for *t*.

If, however, a deaf child should pronounce *t* by placing the point of the tongue against the top of the hard palate, then the passive organ must be shown, thus Ʊⁿ. So also when we represent the *t*-like sound produced during the act of spitting, Ʊ° ("Point of the tongue, shut, against the upper lip.")

In forming the Sanscrit "cerebral *t*" Ʊᶜ ("Point of the tongue, shut against the soft palate") the passive organ, being abnormal, must also be indicated.

In general, the passive organ may be omitted without ambiguity, by adopting the rule that in such cases the active organ shall be considered as applied to that passive organ which is represented by its own symbol in miniature. For example:

ↄ = ↄᵓ ᴜ = ᴜᵘ ∩ = ∩ⁿ C = Cᶜ Ʃ = Ʃ'
D = Dᵓ Ʊ = Ʊᵘ Ω = Ωⁿ ɑ = ɑᶜ Ɒ = Ɒ'

2. I have already alluded to the abbreviation employed to represent the vocalizing position of the larynx. The slit-like aperture (I) alone, is used for the full position—the organs themselves (the vocal cords) being implied. This simple symbol (I) is admirably adapted for combination with other signs into a single character. For example:—

Dᵓ + I = D + I = ϴ
Ʊᵘ + I = Ʊ + I = Ф
Ωⁿ + I = Ω + I = Ω̵
ɑᶜ + I = ɑ + I = ɵ

ↄᵓ + Cᶜ + I (Fig. 6) = ↄ + C + I = ϶ + C = ↄ + Є = ϶ + Є

3. The symbol ʃ ("soft palate") is used to indicate Ʃ' (centre-aperture, between the soft palate and back of the pharynx"). This can be combined with other symbols into a single character. For example:—

(Fig. 8) Dᵓ + Ʃ' + I = D + ʃ + I = [illegible] + I = ϴ + ʃ = [illegible] (Position for *m*).

(Fig. 9) Ʊᵘ + Ʃ' + I = Ʊ + ʃ + I = [illegible] + I = Ф + ʃ = [illegible] (Position for *n*).

(Fig. 10.) ɑᶜ + Ʃ' + I = ɑ + ʃ + I = [illegible] + I = ɵ + ʃ = [illegible] (Position for *ng*).

4. The most difficult case arises when two mouth-positions are simultaneously assumed, Fortunately the curves to be combined are usually of opposite kind so that one can be hooked on to the end of the other.

Thus C + ↄ = ↄ̈ or C̈

The resulting character, however, is of so awkward a shape that another hook is added for the sake of symmetry. Curves of this kind are what my father terms "mixed" symbols. For example:—

C + ↄ = Ɔ a labial position modified by the back of the tongue (English *wh*).

Or = Ϲ a back tongue position modified by the lips. (A labialized German *ch*).

∩ + ᴜ = Ω a front-tongue position modified by the point of the tongue (English *sh*).

Or = Ʊ a point-tongue position modified by the top or "front" of the tongue (English *s*).

5. When two or more positions are simultaneously assumed, the sound may be considered as originating at the point of greatest constriction—the other constrictions merely modifying the effect.

In representing associated positions, therefore, the point of greatest constriction is selected as the base for the compound symbol, and the other positions are indicated in a subordinate manner.

For example, take the positions shown in Fig. 6. In this case we have three associated positions, P, P′, and P″.

Now if P, (the labial position), should happen to be the point of greatest constriction, a rustling noise will be perceived originating at the labial aperture.

This kind of sound is characteristic of air under pressure, escaping through a fine orifice. We can recognize by ear many varieties of the sound for which we have no name. It varies, according to the size of the orifice, and the degree of pressure, from a simple rustling sound—like the rustling of leaves upon a tree, to an intense hiss—like the noise of steam escaping from a locomotive. When the vocal organs yield a noise of this character, we call the effect a "consonant sound."

If, then, the *oo*-like effect produced by the positions shown in Fig, 6, is accompanied by a rustling sound at the labial orifice (P), we call the result a labial "consonant," and not a "vowel" although the voice is heard. The labial position becomes the base for the compound symbol which is then written as follows:—

Ɔ^{ɔ} + C^{c} + I = Ə (English *w*) a labial position modified by the back of the tongue and the throat.

If P′, (Fig. 6), be the point of greatest constriction a rustling sound is also heard, but in this case it originates within the mouth, at the back-tongue position (German *ch*), and the labial aperture simply modifies the effect. This rustling noise characterizes the sound as a "consonant" although the voice is also heard. In this case the back-tongue position becomes the base and the other positions are indicated in a subordinate manner.

C^{c} + Ɔ^{ɔ} + I = Є (German *ch* modified by the lips and vocal cords.

If P″ (Fig. 6), be the point of greatest constriction, the sound heard originates in the glottis. Instead of a continuous rustling noise or hiss, an intermittent effect is produced by the vibration of the vocal cords. The air escapes in a series of puffs that succeed one another with such rapidity as to produce upon the ear the effect of a musical tone. Voice alone is heard without any rustling or whistling accompaniment in the mouth. This characterizes the sound as a "vowel". The sound originates at the position P″, and the mouth positions P, P′, merely modify the effect.

The slit-like aperture between the vocal cords is therefore made the base for the compound symbol; and the mouth positions P, P′, are indicated in a subordinate manner as follows:—

$\mathrm{I} + \mathrm{C}^{c} + \mathrm{Ɔ}^{c} = \mathrm{ɫ}$ (vowel *oo*), a laryngeal position modified by the back of the tongue and the lips.

The vertical line or "vowel stem," represents (I) the slit-like aperture between the vocal cords (P″, Fig. 6), the black dot indicates the back-tongue position C^{c} (P′) · and the horizontal crossbar the labial position $\mathrm{Ɔ}^{\circ}$ (P).

The three sounds represented by the symbols Ə, Є and ɫ, result from almost identical positions of the vocal organs, and in teaching the deaf the sounds themselves may be considered as identical. The subtle distinctions, however, recognized by the ear are faithfully depicted to the eye, in the shape and general appearance of the symbols.

The symbols for *w* (Ə), and the vowel *oo* (ɫ), may be taken as typical of consonant and vowel symbols in general. A curve (*i. e.* a mouth-position), is the characteristic feature of a consonant symbol; and a straight line (I) (the slit-like aperture between the vocal cords), forms the basis of the vowel notation.

In conclusion I may say that the symbols for all the English consonants and vowels have been abbreviated to single signs, and that the phonetical alphabet thus produced is admirably adapted for use in schools for the deaf. The following example of abbreviation may be of interest:

M	*OO*	*N*	
$(\mathrm{D}^{\circ} + \mathrm{C}' + \mathrm{I})$	$(\mathrm{C}^{c} + \mathrm{Ɔ}^{\circ} + \mathrm{I})$	$(\mathrm{U}^{u} + \mathrm{C}' + \mathrm{I})$	= Əɫʊ
Fig. 8.	Fig. 6.	Fig. 9.	

In my next lecture I shall present the symbols of Visible Speech in the way they are taught to the deaf.

Dr. Bell then took charge of some children and illustrated his method of teaching.

Dr. Bell: You must understand that while I claim the privilege of telling you in the forenoon what I want to tell you, I want to do in the afternoon just what you want.

(Dr. Bell here gave an exhibition of the clicks with Miss Black's little girl pupil.)

He said: "It does not matter what sound you get from a child as long as you get a sound. The plan is to follow the child up and symbolize the different sounds made, and get him to remember and repeat the varieties that occur. I go from the known to the unknown. The queer sounds children make are the known sounds to them and the English sounds the unknown. Children like the process, and this to my mind is a proof that it is suited to their condition. There is something wrong about a process that gives pain to a child. It grieves my heart to visit schools for the deaf and find little children constantly corrected for minor defects of pronunciation. The nagging process interrupts the flow of thought through speech, and is apt to dishearten the child in his attempts to speak. I would accept all sounds with approval, and utilize defective sounds in the way I have suggested above."

VISIBLE SPEECH AS TAUGHT TO THE DEAF.

The following Charts are employed for the purpose of explaining to deaf children the meaning of my father's "Visible Speech" symbols.

The elementary symbols shown in Chart I. are compounded in Charts II. and III. to express positions of the vocal organs which yield consonant sounds. In Chart IV. we have other elementary symbols which are combined in Chart V. to express vowel positions. Chart VI. illustrates symbolically the positions of the vocal organs in uttering English consonants, and Chart VII. symbolizes positions that yield English vowels.

CHART I.

The teacher selects some member of her class, and pretends to draw upon the blackboard the profile of the pupil's face. She then looks into the pupil's mouth and proceeds to draw a picture of the interior of the mouth. The whole picture when completed, constitutes a diagram like that shown in Chart I. The teacher then proceeds to test the children's comprehension of the drawing. She points to different parts of the diagram, for example the forehead, nose, upper lip, lower lip, chin, lower part of jaw, throat, etc. The children indicate their comprehension of the diagram by touching the corresponding parts of their own faces. Attention is then directed to the interior of the mouth, and the teacher points to the picture of the upper teeth, upper gum, top of the hard palate, soft palate, etc. The children touch or attempt to touch the corresponding parts of their own mouths. So with the lower organs,—the under teeth, the point of the tongue, the top or "front" part of the tongue, the back of the tongue, etc.

When the comprehension of the class has been well tested, the teacher erases from the blackboard all those parts of the diagram which are shown by dotted lines in Chart I., leaving the Visible Speech symbols in position as shown by the heavy lines.

The teacher points to the fragmentary remains of the picture upon the blackboard, and the pupils recognize the symbols as "the nose," the "under lip," "the point of the tongue," "the top, or front of the tongue," "the back of the tongue," and "the throat." The arrow-head, which represents a sudden emission, or puff, of air from the mouth, is indicated by a sudden motion of the hand away from the mouth.

The next step is to have the pupils recognize the symbols independently of their position on the blackboard. The symbols are therefore written in one line below the fragments of the head (see Chart I.) The heavy lines alone are written, the dotted lines not appearing at all.

The pupils then compare these symbols with the fragments of the drawings above and identify them,—as (1) the throat, (2) the back of the tongue, (3) the top, or front part, of the tongue, (4) the point of the tongue, (5) the under lip, (6) the nose, and (7) puff of air from the mouth.

Finally the upper drawing is entirely removed from the blackboard, and the lower line of symbols alone is left. Each pupil describes these as follows: (1) he touches his throat; (2) he points backwards into his mouth with a little jerk of the hand, indicating a part of the tongue further back in the mouth than he can well touch with his finger; (3) he touches the top, or front part, of his tongue; (4) he touches the tip, or point, of his tongue; (5) he touches his under lip; (6) he touches his nose; (7) he places his hand near his mouth to indicate a sudden emission, or puff, of air.

After these have been mastered, two new symbols, shown at the bottom of Chart I. are introduced. Here again it should be noticed that the symbols drawn on the blackboard consist only of the parts in heavy lines, the parts in dotted lines being omitted. The first of these new marks as you already know, symbolizes a pipe or passage through which air may pass. In the second case the pipe is shut, or stopped up, at one end. The first indicates a narrow central aperture or passage, somewhere in the mouth; the second indicates the complete closure or shutting of the mouth-passage at some part. The idea is of too abstract a character to be explained at once to a deaf child who knows no language; hence

·CHART I·

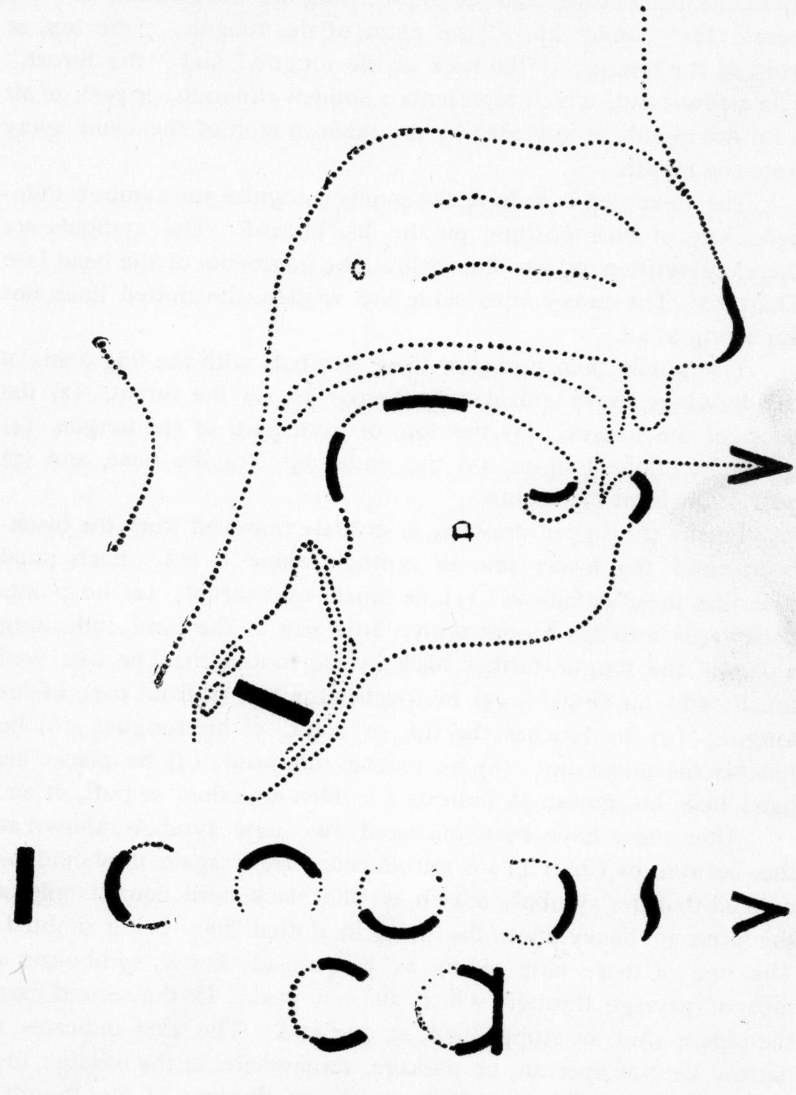

these symbols are taught arbitrarily as positions of the fingers without any attempt being made to explain their significance. As a matter of fact, deaf children come to understand their meaning when applied to the explanation of positions of the mouth.

The pupils are taught to indicate the first symbol at the bottom of Chart I. by holding the thumb and forefinger of the right hand near to one another without touching. This sign we may translate as "centre aperture." The second or "shut" symbol, is shown by bringing the thumb and forefinger together with a shutting action.

We may here notice that the straight line indicating a slit-like aperture between the vocal cords, is used in the sense of "voice." When a deaf child places his hand upon the throat of his teacher he can feel a vibration or tremor in the throat, whenever the voice is sounded. Hence he soon comes to associate the throat sign with a vibration of the vocal cords, and he indicates "voice" by touching his throat.

It should also be noticed that the "nose" sign is really pictorial of the pendulous extremity of the soft palate, and it indicates, as you have already learned, "soft palate depressed" so as to allow air to pass into the nasal passages. When a deaf child places his finger against the nose of his teacher while she pronounces *m*, *n*, or *ng*, he can feel a vibration or tremor of the nostrils, and to him the soft palate symbol means voice or breath passing through the nose.

The symbols shown upon Chart I. are capable of being combined into compound forms, some of which are shown in Charts II. and III.. Before proceeding, however, to the analysis of the compound characters on these Charts it may be well to assign brief names to the elementary symbols of Chart I.: these we can use to designate the gestures or signs employed by the deaf child which have been explained above.

In the following Charts, I shall refer to the symbols at the bottom of Chart I. as—

1. Voice. 2. Back. 3. Front. 4. Point. 5. Lip. 6. Nose. 7. Puff of air. 8. Centre-aperture. 9. Shut.

CHART II.

The symbols on this Chart are named by the deaf child by analyzing them into the elementary symbols of which they are composed. We may translate his signs as follows:—

First line.—1. Lip centre-aperture. 2. Point centre-aperture. 3. Front centre-aperture. 4. Back centre-aperture.

Second line.—1. Lip centre-aperture. Voice. 2. Point centre aperture, Voice. 3. Front centre-aperture, Voice. 4. Back centre-aperture, Voice.

Third line.—1. Lip centre-aperture, Nose. 2. Point centre-aperture, Nose. 3. Front centre-aperture, Nose. 4. Back centre-aperture, Nose.

Fourth line.—1. Lip centre-aperture, Voice, Nose. 2. Point centre-aperture, Voice, Nose. 3. Front centre-aperture, Voice, Nose. 4. Back centre-aperture, Voice, Nose.

Fifth line.—1. Lip shut. 2. Point shut. 3. Front shut. 4. Back shut.

Sixth line.—1. Lip shut, Voice. 2. Point shut, Voice. 3. Front shut, Voice. 4. Back shut, Voice.

Seventh line.—1. Lip shut, Nose. 2. Point shut, Nose. 3. Front shut, Nose. 4. Back shut, Nose.

Eighth line.—1. Lip shut, Voice, Nose. 2. Point shut, Voice, Nose. 3. Front shut, Voice, Nose. 4. Back shut, Voice, Nose.

Long before a class has finished describing these symbols, the pupils begin to obtain the idea that the symbols are directions to do something with the mouth. For example, when they describe the first symbol in the fifth line, "Lip shut," some of them usually shut their lips. After the whole Chart has been described, it then becomes the teacher's duty to make the children understand that the compound symbols they have been describing indicate positions of the mouth. The teacher directs attention to her mouth while she assumes some of the positions symbolized. For example, she describes *seriatim* the symbols in the first line.

1. "Lip centre-aperture." She places her lips close together leaving a small aperture between them. She then takes a pupil's hand and blows through this small centre-aperture against his hand. The resulting sound is not an English element of speech, but is the sound produced by blowing to cool something.

2. She describes the next symbol, "Point centre-aperture." With her hand she lifts up the point of her tongue and brings it into position against the upper gum, and makes the pupil look into her mouth and observe that there is a small aperture or hole between the point of her tongue and the upper gum. She then, without moving her tongue, blows through the point centre-aperture against the pupil's hand. The resultant sound is that of the French *r*, in the word *theâtre*, or the English *r*, (non-vocal), in the word *tree*.

In a similar manner she shows that in pronouncing the third symbol "Front centre-aperture," the tongue is humped up in the middle, leaving a small centre passage or channel over the front of the tongue, through which she can blow against the pupil's hand. The resultant sound is that of the letter *h* in the word *hue*.

4. In pronouncing the fourth symbol she pushes her tongue towards the back part of her mouth with her hand, and shows that her tongue remains back when her hand is removed. She then lets the pupil feel that air can be blown upon his hand without moving the tongue. The resulting sound is that of the German *ch* in the word *nach*.

Proceeding next to the second line:—

1. She shows that the first symbol, "Lip center-aperture, Voice," is the same as the first symbol in the first line, "Lip centre-aperture," excepting that a straight line is placed within the curve. She shows then that the lips are in the same position, but that a tremor or vibration can be felt in the throat which could not be felt when the other symbol was sounded. She takes the two hands of her pupil and places one against her throat, and holds the other in front of her mouth while she produces "Lip centre-aperture, Voice." The pupil sees the small centre-aperture between the lips, and feels the emission of air against his hand, and also perceives the trembling of the throat when the voice is sounded. The resulting sound is the German *w* in the word *wie*.

2. In a similar manner, keeping one of the pupil's hands on her throat and the other in front of the mouth, she produces the second symbol in the second line, "Point centre-aperture, Voice," contrasting it with the second symbol in the first line, which has no voice. He sees the centre-aperture over the point of the tongue, and feels the vibration of the voice and the emission of air from the mouth. The resulting sound is that of the letter *r* in the word *run*.

3. In a similar manner she exemplifies the third symbol in the second line, "Front centre-aperture, Voice." The resultant sound is that of the consonant *y* in *you*. In teaching the deaf, this may be considered identical with the vowel *ee*.

4. The fourth symbol in the second line, "Back centre-aperture, Voice," is shown to be the same as the German *ch* (Back centre-aperture), excepting that a vibration is felt in the throat.

Proceeding next to the eighth line:—

1. The teacher describes the first symbol, "Lip shut, Voice, Nose." In forming this sound the lips are shut and the voice is

· CHART II ·

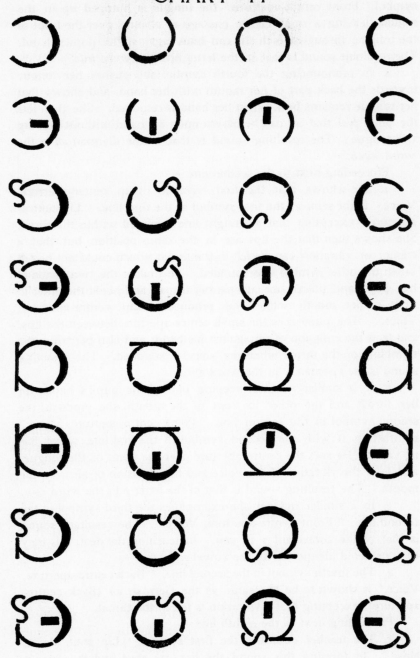

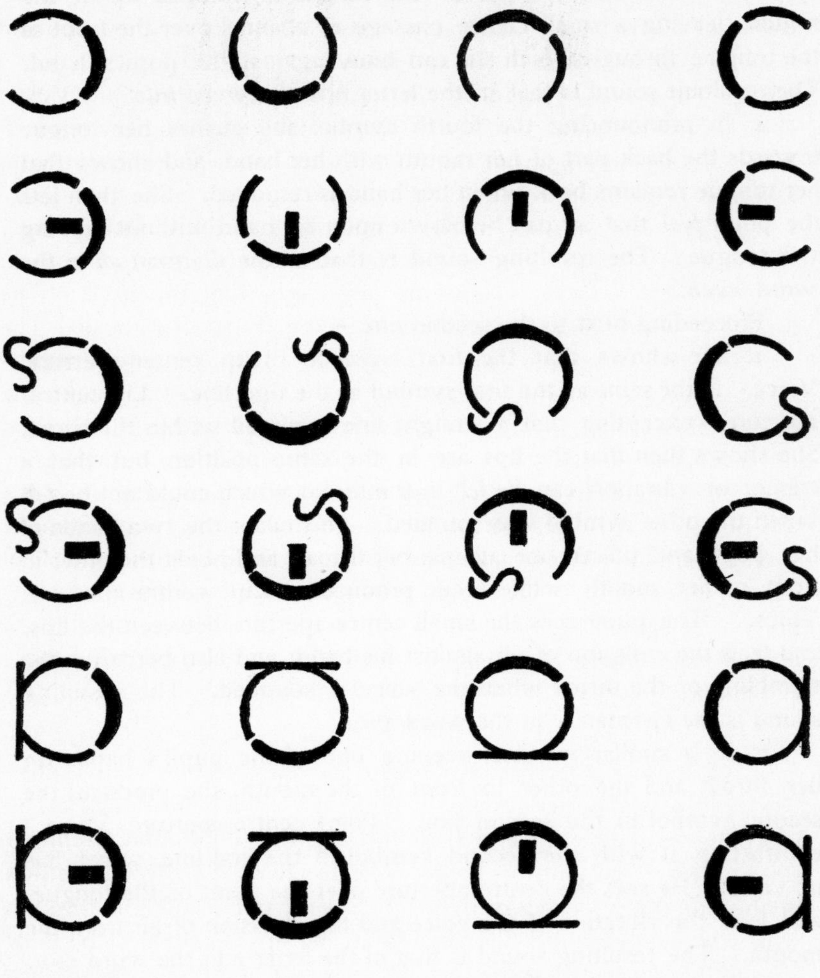

passed through the nose. She places one of the pupil's hands against her throat, and the other against her nose, and produces the sound of the letter *m*. The pupil sees the closure of the lips and feels a vibration in the throat and nose.

2. The second symbol in the eighth line, "Point shut, Voice, Nose," represents the position of the organs in forming the letter *n*. The pupil sees the point of the tongue shut against the upper gum and feels a vibration in the throat and nose.

4. The last symbol in the eighth line, "Back shut, Voice, Nose," expresses the position of the organs when producing *ng* in such a word as *sing*. Here the pupil sees that the back of the tongue is raised, and feels a vibration in the throat and nose. The object of this exemplification is simply to make the pupils understand what the symbols mean, and not to get them to make the sounds themselves. Still, the children generally try to imitate what the teacher does, and of course, in some cases they fail because they have not yet acquired control over their vocal organs. As it is not the object of their teacher at this stage to cause the pupil to make sounds, she should not take any notice of their failures for fear of discouraging them. She should be satisfied with evidences of comprehension as to the meaning of the symbols. Most children are able to take Charts I. and II. in one lesson. After reviewing these at a subsequent time the third Chart is explained.

CHART III.

The pupil's attention is directed to the symbol "Lip centre-aperture" (see the first symbol in Chart II.), which he describes by touching the under lip and then holding the thumb and forefinger close together without touching. The teacher then directs attention to the mouth, and shows that there is only one small hole through which the air passes. She then holds her lips together in the middle and allows air to escape through two side apertures, one at each corner of the mouth, showing the pupil that now there are two holes through which the air escapes instead of one. This fact she symbolizes by writing two "Lip centre-aperture" symbols one above the other, ↄ ↄ thus, forming a character somewhat like the Arabic numeral 3. This the pupil describes by touching his lip, and then holding near the thumb two fingers, instead of one alone, indicating that the aperture is divided into two parts. Thus the thumb and forefinger held together indicate one central aperture, and the thumb held near the fore and middle fingers indicates "divided aperture."

Turning now to Chart III. the symbols are described as follows:

First line.—1. Lip divided-aperture. 2. Point divided-aperture. 3. Front divided-aperture. 4. Back divided-aperture

Second line.—1. Lip divided-aperture, Voice. 2. Point divided-aperture, Voice. 3. Front divided-aperture, Voice. 4. Back divided-aperture, Voice.

The second symbol in the second line, "Point divided-aperture, Voice," expresses the position of the tongue in forming the sound of *l* in such a word as *love*. The point of the tongue is placed against the upper gum, and the voice is passed through two side apertures, one on each side of the tongue. The symbols in the third, fourth, fifth, and sixth lines are what my father terms "mixed" symbols, involving two positions of the organs assumed simultaneously. The first symbol in the the third line is composed of a large "Lip centre-aperture" symbol with a small "Back centre-aperture" hooked on to one end of the curve. For the sake of symmetry another small "Back centre-aperture" is attached to the other end of the curve, but this has no organic significance. This compound symbol expresses the position of the organs in sounding the English element represented by the letters *wh* in such a word as *whistle*. The back of the tongue is in the position for the German *ch* (Back centre-aperture), while at the same time a small centre-aperture is formed by the lips. The labial aperture being more obstructive than the back aperture, characterizes the sound as a labial letter. For this reason the "Lip centre-aperture sign is made the most prominent part of the compound symbol. Deaf pupils describe this symbol as "Lip centre-aperture, Back centre-aperture."

Proceeding now with the description of the remaining symbols upon Chart III. we have:—

Third line.—1. Lip centre-aperture, Back centre-aperture. 2. Point centre-aperture, Front centre-aperture. 3. Front centre-aperture, Point centre-aperture. 4. Back centre-aperture, Lip centre-aperture.

Fourth line.—1. Lip centre-aperture, Back centre-aperture, Voice. 2. Point centre-aperture, Front centre-aperture, Voice. 3. Front centre-aperture, Point centre-aperture, Voice. 4. Back centre-aperture, Lip centre-aperture, Voice.

Fifth line.—1. Lip divided-aperture, Back centre-aperture. 2. Point divided-aperture, Front centre-aperture. 3. Front divided-aperture, Point centre-aperture. 4. Back divided-aperture, Lip centre-aperture.

Sixth line.—1. Lip divided-aperture, Back centre-aperture, Voice. 2. Point divided-aperture, Front centre-aperture, Voice. 3. Front divided-aperture, Point centre-aperture, Voice. 4. Back divided-aperture, Lip centre-aperture, Voice.

Numerous other compound symbols might be built up out of the elementary signs shown in Chart I., expressing both possible and impossible positions of the organs. The forms shown in Charts II. and III. are not intended to be pronounced by the pupil, but are given simply as exercises in analysis. If the pupil can be made to understand the meaning of the compound symbols by analyzing them into their elementary forms, Visible Speech becomes a symbolic language, whereby any imaginable position of the vocal organs may be expressed, so as to be understood by the children.

The remaining symbols on Chart III. seventh line, are throat symbols. They picture various conditions of the glottis.

1. The first character, shaped like the letter O, pictures a wide aperture in the throat. The vocal cords are wide apart, leaving a large opening between them through which air may freely pass without obstruction. This is the condition of the glottis in uttering the letter *h*, and all non-vocal or breath consonants. The letter *h* may, indeed, be considered as the non-vocal or breath form of a vowel. It has just as many different sounds as there are vowels. Pronounce such words as *he, hay, ha, hoe,* and *who;* it will be observed that the mouth-position for the sound of *h* is different in each word. *H* only occurs as an element of speech before a vowel. Under such circumstances the mouth position for *h* is the same as for the succeeding vowel, but the opening in the glottis is so wide as to allow the breath to pass into the mouth without sensible obstruction in the throat.

2. The second symbol in the seventh line, pictures a smaller aperture in the throat than the first. The vocal cords are brought near enough together to obstruct in some degree the passage of air between them, giving rise to a rustling sort of sound which is universally denominated "whisper." This is the condition of the glottis when we whisper vowel sounds. This position of the throat also may be assumed in uttering consonants, thus giving rise to the "whispered" consonants, which in some languages are significant elements of speech, quite distinct in meaning from the "breath" and "voiced" consonants of similar formation occurring in the same languages.

3. We have already become familiar with the third symbol in the seventh line, as the representative of voice. It pictures a still smaller aperture in the throat than either of the preceding. The vocal cords are placed parallel to one another, and the aperture between them is reduced to a mere slit (pictured by a straight line). In this condition of the glottis the passage of air through the slit-like aperture occasions a vibration of the vocal cords, producing voice. This is the condition of the glottis in uttering vocal consonants and vowels.

4. The fourth symbol in the seventh line, pictures complete closure of the glottis. The vocal cords are pressed together so as to completely shut the aperture between them, and prevent the escape of air. This is the condition of the glottis aimed at by singers in practicing what is called the "*coup de glotte.*" It also occurs as an element of speech in certain dialects. For example: In the Scotch dialect as spoken in Glasgow, "Throat shut" is substituted for *t* (Point shut) in such words as butter, water, etc. In English also it occurs as an unrecognized element of speech in words commencing with vowels. In ordinary utterance every syllable really commences with a consonant. When words are supposed to begin with vowels, the "Throat shut" consonant really precedes the vowel sound, although it is not usually recognized as an element of speech by orthoepists. Pronounce with considerable force the names of the five vowel letters *a, e, i, o, u*. A closure of the glottis takes place before each vowel, excepting the last. The "Throat shut" consonant precedes the vowels *a, e, i,* and *o;* but *u* is preceded by the consonant *y*. Indeed, the name of the vowel might have been spelled *you* without affecting the pronunciation. The "Throat shut" consonant, followed by a forcible emission of air from the lungs, is familiar to every one in the form of a cough.

The meaning of the throat symbols shown in the seventh line, is explained to deaf children in the following way:

1. Touch the throat, and then hold the two hands together palm to palm, curving the fingers so as to cause the space between the hands to assume the shape of the first symbol. The idea to be conveyed is, that the aperture in the throat is somewhat of that shape, and very large.

2. Touch the throat, and then hold the hands together palm to palm, as before, but reduce the space between the hands so as to cause the aperture to assume the shape of the second symbol. The

·CHART· III·

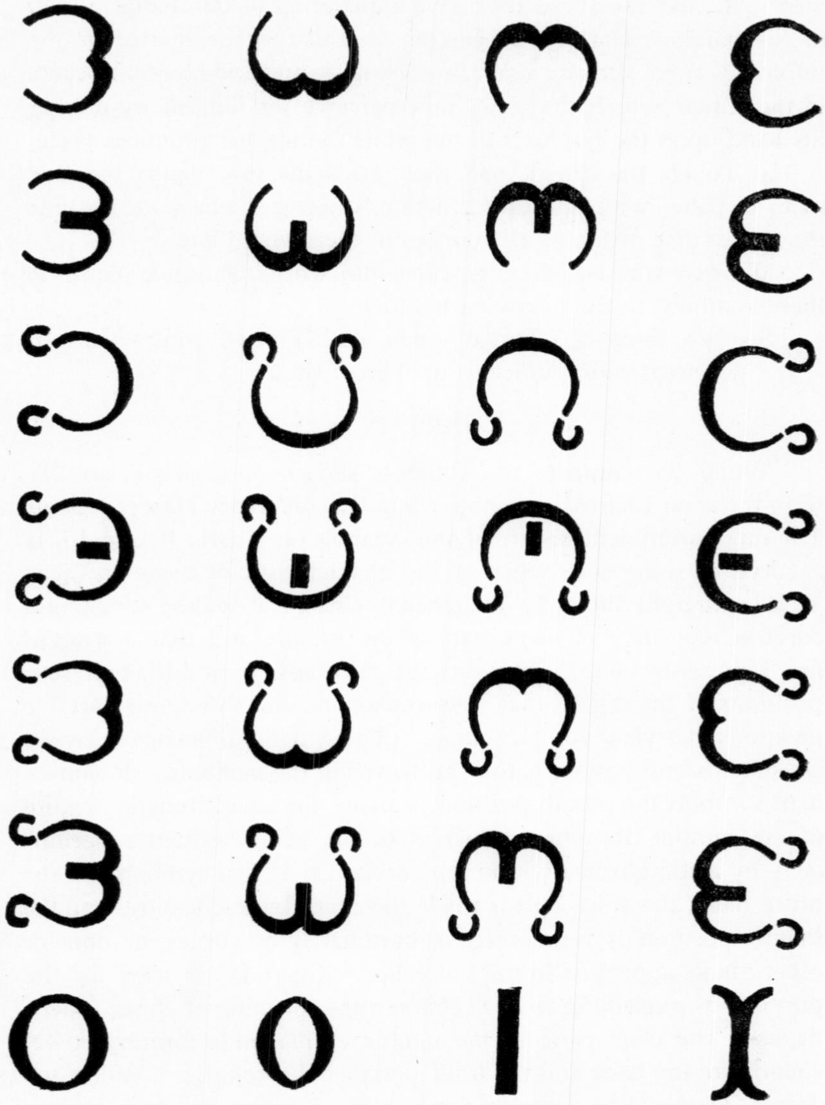

idea to be conveyed, is that the aperture in the throat is more contracted than in the former case.

3. Touch the throat, and hold the hands together palm to palm, as before, so that the aperture between the hands is reduced to a mere slit. At the same time give a quivering or trembling motion to the hands. The idea to be conveyed, is that the aperture in the throat is a mere slit, and that a trembling or quivering motion occurs in the throat which the pupil may perceive for himself by placing his hand upon the teacher's throat while the teacher produces voice.

4. Touch the throat, and then press the two hands together palm to palm, with a shutting action, causing the hands to assume the appearance of the fourth symbol in the seventh line.

We may translate these gestures into words, and give names to these symbols, in the following manner:—

Seventh line.—1. Throat open. 2. Throat contracted. 3. Throat a-slit (Voice). 4. Throat shut.

CHART IV.

When we compare the symbols shown on Charts II. and III. with those on Chart V., we notice a radical difference between them. The most prominent feature of the symbols on Charts II. and III. is a curve of some sort, whereas the characteristic of those on Chart V. is a straight line. By reference to Chart I. it will be seen that a curve is indicative of some part of the mouth, and that a straight line represents voice. The symbols on Charts II. and III. represent positions of the organs that yield consonant, and those on Chart V., positions that yield vowel, sounds. The generic difference between consonants and vowels is thus portrayed in the symbols. In consonant symbols the mouth position is made the characteristic feature of the symbol, the voice where it occurs being written subordinately by a straight line within the curve. In vowel symbols, on the other hand, the voice sign is made the characteristic feature, and the mouth position is represented subordinately by curves, or dots or other marks appended to the voice line. Chart IV. is used for the purpose of explaining to deaf children the meaning of these appendages. The chief parts of the tongue employed in forming vowel sounds are the back and the front parts of the tongue. When we drawa vertical line centrally through the diagram on Chart IV., we find that a dot or other mark on the right-hand side of the line rests on the front part of the tongue, whereas a mark on the left-hand side of the line rests on the back of the tongue. In vowel symbols a

·CHART IV·

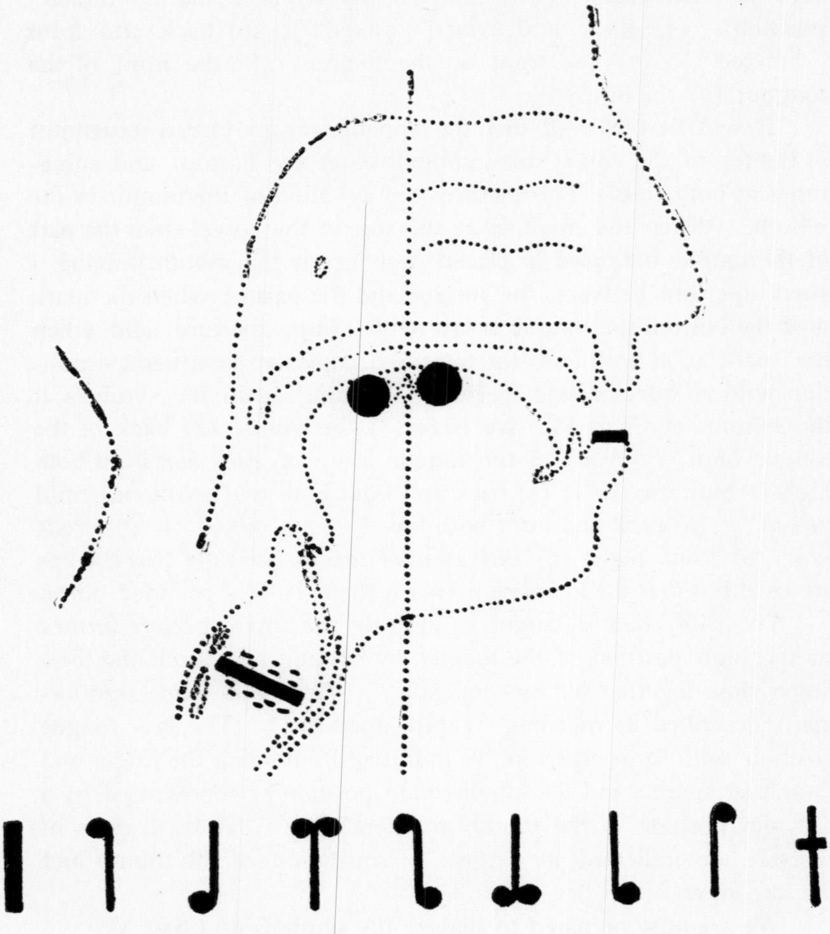

mark on the right-hand side of the voice line indicates the front part of the tongue, a mark on the left indicates the back of the tongue, and a short horizontal line drawn across the vowel stem indicates that the lips are employed. Thus the symbols at the bottom of Chart IV. indicate (1) the voice; (2) the back of the tongue; (3) the back of the tongue; (4) both back and front of the tongue used simultaneously; [this is what my father terms a "mixed" position]. (5) Back and front ["mixed"]; (6) back and front ["mixed"]; (7) the front of the tongue; (8) the front of the tongue; (9) the lips.

It will be observed that the appendages are placed sometimes at the top of the vowel stem, sometimes at the bottom, and sometimes at both ends. This pictures the elevation of the tongue in the mouth. When the mark is at the top of the vowel stem the part of the tongue indicated is placed high up in the mouth, leaving a small aperture between the tongue and the palate; when the mark is at the bottom the tongue is low with a large aperture; and when the mark is at both ends the tongue occupies an intermediate position with an intermediate aperture. Reading again the symbols at the bottom of Chart IV., we have (1) the voice; (2) back of the tongue high; (3) back of the tongue low; (4) back and front both high ["high mixed"]; (5) back and front both mid positions ["mid mixed"]; (6) back and front both low ["low mixed"]; (7) front low; (8) front high; (9) this symbol means not only that the lips are used but that the aperture between them is of a rounded form.

The deaf child is taught to indicate the small aperture formed by the high position of the tongue, by holding his thumb and forefinger close together without touching. (This is the same sign formerly described as meaning "centre aperture.") The low tongue position with large aperture, is indicated by holding the finger and thumb far apart.; and the intermediate position is represented by a half-way position of the thumb and forefinger. Thus, degrees of aperture are indicated by degrees of separation of the thumb and the forefinger.

We are now prepared to analyze the symbols on Chart V.

CHART V.—Vowels.

The vowels on Chart V. may be divided into four groups of nine symbols each:—

First Group.—*Primary Vowels.*

Reading downwards we have:—

First line.—1. High Back. 2. Mid Back. 3. Low Back.
Second line.—1. High Mixed. 2. Mid Mixed. 3. Low Mixed.
Third line.—1. High Front. 2. Mid Front. 3. Low Front.

SECOND GROUP.—*Wide Vowels.*

Reading downwards we have:—

First line.—1. High Back Wide. 2. Mid Back Wide. 3. Low Back Wide.

Second line.—1. High mixed Wide. 2. Mid Mixed Wide. 3. Low Mixed Wide.

Third line.—1. High Front Wide. 2. Mid Front Wide. 3. Low Front Wide.

THIRD GROUP.—*Primary Round Vowels.*

Reading downwards we have:—

First line.—1. High Back Round. 2. Mid Back Round. 3. Low Back Round.

Second line.—1. High Mixed Round. 2. Mid Mixed Round. 3. Low Mixed Round.

Third Line.—1. High Front Round. 2. Mid Front Round. 3. Low Front Round.

FOURTH GROUP.—*Wide Round Vowels.*

Reading downwards we have:—

First line.—1. High Back Wide Round. 2. Mid Back Wide Round. 3. Low Back Wide Round.

Second line.—1. High Mixed Wide Round. 2. Mid Mixed Wide Round. 3. Low Mixed Wide Round.

Third line.—1. High Front Wide Round. 2. Mid Front Wide Round. 3. Low Front Wide Round.

Wide vowels differ from primary vowels by a slight widening of the oral passage; for example: Contrast the "high front" vowel (*ea* in the word *eat*), with the "high front wide" vowel (*i* in the word *it*). The oral passage for the latter is slightly larger than for *ee*, and Prof. Melville Bell believes also that the back part of the mouth, or the cavity of the pharynx, is more expanded in wide vowels than in primary. Widening the oral passage is indicated by a hook instead of a dot. Groups III. and IV. are rounded vowels, that is, the passage between the lips is of a rounded form.

Deaf children describe these symbols by using the signs already mentioned in describing Chart IV., and we may translate their signs for the symbols on Chart V. as follows:

First Group.—*Primary Vowels.*

Reading downwards we have:—

First line.—1. Voice, Back small-aperture. 2. Voice, Back mid-aperture. 3. Voice, Back large-aperture.

Second line.—1. Voice, Back small-aperture, Front small-aperture. 2. Voice, Back mid-aperture, Front mid-aperture. 3. Voice, Back large-aperture, Front large-aperture.

Third line.—1. Voice, Front small-aperture. 2. Voice, Front mid-aperture. 3. Voice, Front large-aperture.

Second Group.—*Wide Vowels.*

In teaching deaf children, the symbols of this group are considered as identical with those of Group I., and are described in the same manner. When the pupils have become familiar with the analysis of Visible Speech symbols, they are shown, by means of the thumb and forefinger, that the position symbolized in Group II. have a slightly wider aperture than the corresponding positions in Group I.

Prof. Melville Bell's conception of the expansion of the pharynx during the utterance of wide vowels, is a difficult one to convey to deaf children who know no language; I have, therefore, not attempted to do more than convey the idea that the mouth passage for wide vowels, is slightly wider than for primary vowels, so that the primary and wide symbols, taken together, represent six degrees of aperture; for example: Take the front vowels, commencing with the smallest aperture and ending with the largest, we have the following series of apertures:—

1. High Front.
2. High Front Wide.
3. Mid Front.
4. Mid Front Wide.
5. Low Front.
6. Low Front Wide.

Third Group.—*Primary Round Vowels.*

Reading downwards we have:—

First line.—1. Voice, Back small-aperture, Lip, small-aperture. 2. Voice, Back mid-aperture, Lip mid-aperture. 3. Voice, Back large-aperture, Lip large-aperture.

Second line.—1. Voice, Back small-aperture, Front small-aperture, Lip small-aperture. 2. Voice, Back mid-aperture, Front mid-aperture, Lip mid-aperture. 3. Voice, Back large-aperture, Front large-aperture, Lip large-aperture.

· CHART V ·

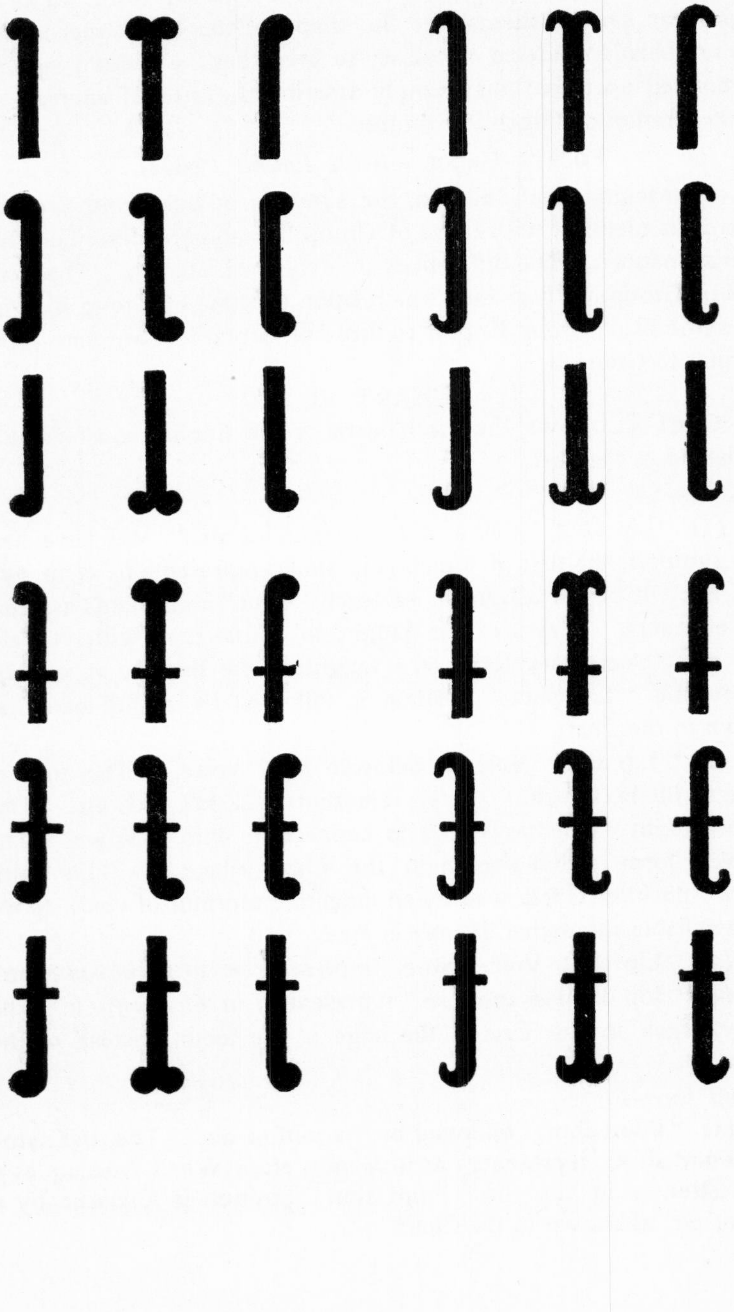

Third line.—1. Voice, Front small-aperture, Lip small-aperture. 2. Voice, Front mid-aperture, Lip mid-aperture. 3. Voice, Front large-aperture, Lip large-aperture.

The labial apertures described are of a rounded form, but as the pupils can see for themselves the shape of the labial apertures, it has not been considered necessary to give them a distinct sign for a rounded aperture; they simply describe the size of aperture by the separation of finger and thumb.

FOURTH GROUP.—*Wide Round Vowels.*

In teaching deaf children, the symbols of this group are considered as identical with those of Group III., and are described in a similar manner. The differences are explained later on. The symbols of Group IV. bear the same relation to those of Group III., that the symbols of Group II. bear to those of Group I. (See note above relating to Group II.

CHART VI.

Chart VI. shows the mechanism or the English consonants as explained to the deaf.

First line:—

(1) "Lip shut," followed by a "puff of air." We have here two symbols, the first of which (Lip shut), represents *p*, as in *put, cup*, etc. It is not advisable to teach "shut" consonants as separate elements. They are best taught in connection with vowels. The most elementary form of *p* taught, is the final *p*, as in *cup*, where the "Lip shut" position is followed by a puff of air, as shown in the Chart.

(2) "Lip shut, Voice," followed by "voice." The first of these symbols (Lip shut, voice), represents *b* in *but, cub*, etc. This is not taught elementarily, but in connection with a vowel. The simplest form is that shown in the Chart where the "Lip shut, Voice" position is followed by an indefinite murmur of voice, forming a syllable somewhat like *bir* in *bird.*

(3) "Lip shut, Voice, Nose," represents *m* in *man, come*, etc.

(4) "Lip divided-aperture," represents *f* in *file, luff*, etc. The upper organ in this case is the edge of the teeth, instead of the upper lip.

Second line:—

(1) "Point shut," followed by "a puff of air." The first symbol (Point shut), represents *t* as in *to, not*, etc. When *t* occurs as a final letter, as in *not*, the "Point shut" position is followed by a puff of air, as shown in the Chart.

(2) "Point shut, Voice," followed by "Voice." The first symbol (Point shut, Voice), represents *d*, as in *do, nod,* etc. In the symbols shown in the Chart, the "Point shut, Voice" position is followed by an indefinite murmur of voice, thus representing a syllable somewhat like *dir* in *dirk*.

(3) "Point shut, Voice, Nose" represents *n*, as in *no, nun,* etc.

(4) "Lip divided-aperture, Voice" represents *v*, as in *vie, love,* etc.

Third line:—

(1) "Back shut" followed by a "puff of air." The first symbol (Back shut), represents *k*, as in *key, sick,* etc. When *k* occurs as a final letter, as in *sick*, the "Back shut" position is followed by a puff of air, as shown in the Chart.

(2) "Back shut, Voice," followed by "Voice." The first o these symbols (Back shut, Voice, represents *g*, as in *go, log,* etc. The "Back shut, Voice" position is followed by an indefinite murmur of Voice, forming a syllable somewhat like *gir* in *girl*.

(3) "Back shut, Voice, Nose," represents *ng*, as in *lung, tongue,* etc.

(4) "Lip centre-aperture, Back centre-aperture," represents *wh*, as in *whet*. It is taught to the deaf as "Back centre-aperture" (German *ch*), with the lips rounded as in the act of whistling. In obtaining this sound from a deaf child, it is found essential to direct attention to the "Back centre-aperture position."

Fourth line:—

(1) "Point divided-aperture, Voice" represents *l*, in *lull*.

(2) "Point divided-aperture, Front centre-aperture" represents *th* as in *thin, kith,* etc.

(3) "Point divided-aperture, Front centre-aperture, Voice" represents *th* as in *then, with,* etc.

(4) "Lip centre-aperture, Back centre-aperture, Voice" represents *w* in the word *wet*. In teaching the deaf it is essential to direct attention to the "Back centre-aperture" position, and the sound is taught as identical with the vowel *oo* in *pool*.

Fifth line:—

(1) "Point centre-aperture, Front centre-aperture" represents *s*, as in *sown, hiss,* etc.

(2) "Point centre-aperture, Front centre-aperture, Voice, represents *z* in *zone*, and *s* in *his*.

·CHART VI·

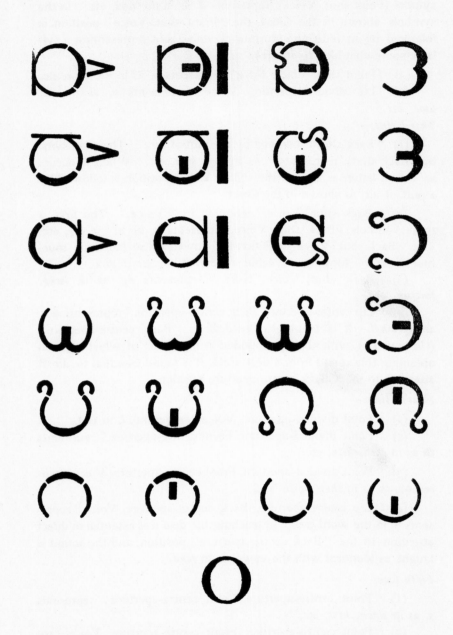

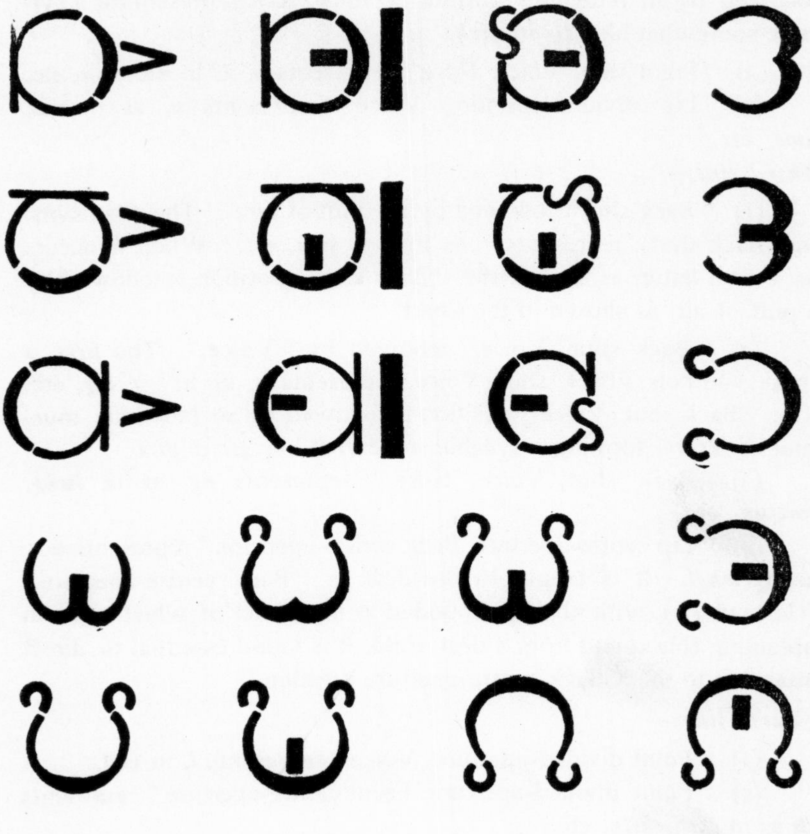

(3) "Front centre-aperture, Point centre-aperture" represents ***sh*** as in *she,* and *s,* in *assure.* It also occurs after "Point shut" in such a word as *church* (tshurtsh).

(4) "Front centre-aperture, Point centre-aperture, Voice" represents *s* in *measure,* and *z* in *azure.* It is heard in *j* and in *g* soft, after "Point shut Voice" in such a word as *judge* (dzhudzh).

Sixth line:—

(1) "Front centre-aperture" represents the sound given to ***h*** in ***hue,*** for which we have no letter. As it is the non-vocal form of the consonant *y,* it may be represented by *yh.* It also occurs after non-vocal consonants, as in *few* (f*y*hoo), *tune* (t*y*hoon), *cue* (k*y*hoo).

(2) "Front centre-aperture, Voice" represents *y* in the word *you.* In teaching the deaf it is considered as identical with the vowel *e.*

(3) "Point centre-aperture." This sound has no letter, and may be represented by ***rh,*** as it is the non-vocal form of *r.* The deaf are taught that the letter *r* has this sound when it comes after a non-vocal consonant, as in *pry* (p*rh*y), *try* (t*rh*y), *cry* (c*rh*y).

(4) "Point centre-aperture, Voice" represents *r* in such a word as *run,* also *r* after a vocal consonant, *bride, dry,* etc.

Seventh line:—

"Throat large-aperture" represents *h* in such words ***heat, hit, hate, head, hat, hoot, hook, hope, hall, hot, half, hurl, hut, high, how, hoist,*** etc.

CHART VII.

The symbols in Chart VII. represent the positions for English vowel sounds.

First line:—

(1) "High Back Wide, Round" represents the vowel heard in the following words: *foot, put,* etc.

(2) "High Back, Round" represents the vowel heard in ***pool, move, through, true, flew,*** etc.

(3) "High Front represents the vowel heard in ***eel, eat, field, key, seize,*** etc.

(4) "High Front Wide" represents the vowel heard in *ill, build,* etc.

Second line:—

(1) "Mid Back, Round," followed by a glide towards "High Back, Round," represents the diphthongal vowel heard in ***pole, coal, soul, dough, bowl,*** etc.

(2) "Mid Front," followed by a glide towards "High Front," r presents the diphthongal vowel heard in *ale, ail, eight, great, say, they,* etc.

Third line:—

(1) "Low Back Wide, Round" represents the vowel heard in *doll, what,* etc.

(2) "Low Back, Round" represents the vowel heard in *all, paul, paw, thought,* etc.

(3) "Low Front" represents the vowel heard in *shell, head, said,* etc.

(4) "Low Front Wide" represents the vowel heard in *shall, hat, can, and,* etc.

Fourth line:—

(1) "Low Back Wide" represents the vowel heard in *ah, father,* etc.

(2) "Mid Back Wide" represents the vowel heard in *ask, path,* etc.

(3) "Low Mixed Wide" represents the vowel heard in *her, pearl, girl, fur,* etc.

(4) "Mid Back" represents the vowel heard in *gull, come, rough,* etc.

Fifth line:—

(1) "Mid Back Wide," followed by a glide towards "High Front," represents the diphthongal vowel heard in *pile, sleight, buy, eye,* etc.

(2) "Mid Back Wide," followed by a glide towards "High Back Round," represents the diphthongal vowel heard in *cow, bough, round,* etc.

(3) "Low Back Round," followed by a glide towards "High Front," represents the diphthongal vowel heard in *oil, boy,* etc.

The sound of *h* only occurs before a vowel, and it is advisable to give the deaf pupil the idea that there are as many sounds of *h* as there are vowel sounds. Defective pronunciation results from the attempt to give a uniform value to the sound. The deaf pupil is taught that the mouth position for *h* is always the same as that of the succeeding vowel; in fact, that *h* is the *breath form* of the succeeding vowel. For example: Contrast *h* in *he,* with that in

CHART VII

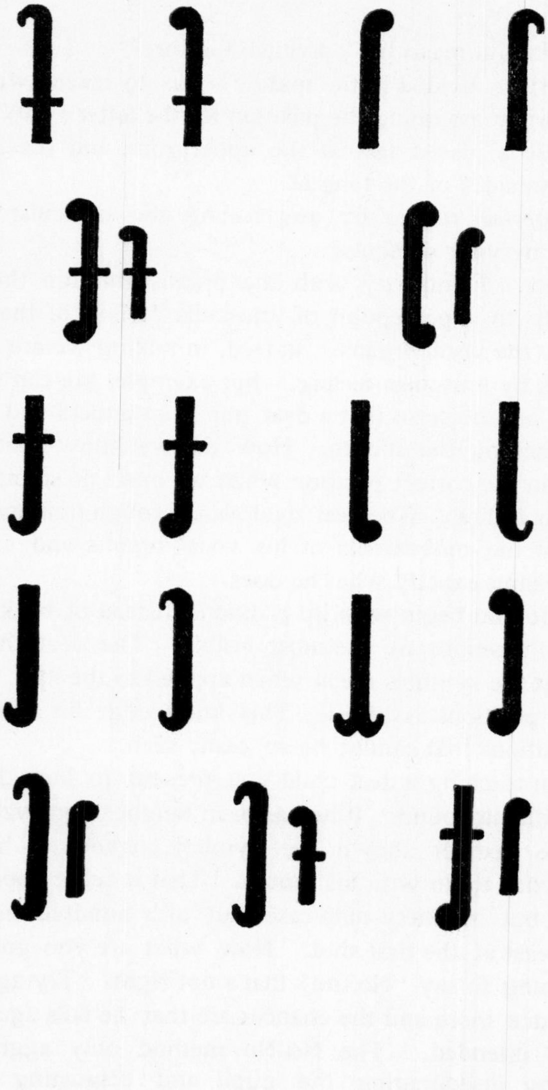

who (hoo). In the former case the mouth position for *h* is the same as that for the vowel *ee*, in the latter it is the same as that for the vowel *oo*.

Do you describe the word "Mixed?"

We do not use the word "Mixed" in teaching the deaf, but describe in detail the positions that are mixed. Thus, we describe my father's "Lip-mixed" consonant as "Lip centre-aperture, Back centre-aperture."

What do you mean by "divided-aperture?"

An aperture divided in the middle so as to leave two orifices. For example: In assuming the position for the letter *l* (ω), the point of the tongue is placed against the upper gum, and the air passes out over both sides of the tongue.

Can a person realize by any feeling the muscular condition represented by your symbols?

Certainly. Familiarity with the organs through the use of a mirror leads to a perception of muscular feeling of the positions assumed by the vocal organs. Indeed, in talking we are all guided more or less by muscular feeling. For example, we can talk without making any noise so that a deaf pupil can understand what we say by watching the mouth. How do we know that our vocal organs are in the correct position when we make no sound? Surely by muscular feeling. The deaf child also, through training, becomes conscious of the movements of his vocal organs and can tell by muscular feeling exactly what he does.

Why do you begin with lip positions instead of back positions?

The lip positions are the most visible. The deaf child understands what the symbols mean when applied to the lips, because he can see the positions assumed. This knowledge he applies to the interior positions that cannot be so easily seen.

Now in teaching a deaf child you present to him the symbol for some difficult sound. If he has been taught to analyze the symbols in the manner shown, the symbol conveys to his mind a direction what to do with his mouth. That is what your pupil has to aim at, but in ninety-nine cases out of a hundred he may not get it, at least at the first shot. Now what are you going to do? Are you going to say "No, no! that's not right. Try again?" Let him try once more and the chances are that he fails again to give the sound intended. The No-No method only aggravates the difficulty by discouraging the pupil and disgusting him with articulation.

Learning to speak is like learning to shoot. Now, suppose you aim at a target for the first time, and fail to hit it, and you are simply told "No, no; that's not right. Try again." Well, suppose you do try again. The chances are that you fail, and if you were simply told once more that you didn't hit the bull's eye, you are no further advanced than you were before. That's not the way to learn to shoot. You must know *where your bullet struck when you failed,* so as to see the relation between the point struck and the point you intended to hit. The knowledge of that relation will guide your next shot. For example: If you know that you hit too far to the right, why your next shot is aimed more to the left, and perhaps flies clear of the target on the other side. If, then, you are told the result of this shot also, you make due allowances the next time you try. You may fail a hundred times. Now you go a little to the right, now a little to the left, sometimes too high, sometimes too low; but your knowledge of the effect of each shot causes you to make unconscious allowances, so that, little by little, you come nearer the bull's eye until at last you hit it. When you can hit the bull's eye every time, you have mastered your instrument—the gun—and can hit any other bull's eye with equal ease.

The No-No method, besides discouraging the beginner fails to give the very information that is necessary for his progress. The deaf child must know *what he did when he failed,* and the relation of the position struck to the bull's eye. The knowledge of that relation will guide him in his next attempt. For example: If he knows that his tongue was too far forward in the mouth, in his next attempt he aims at having his tongue further back and probably gets too far in that direction. If, then, he is told the result of this attempt also, he makes due allowances the next time he tries. He may fail a hundred times. Now the position may be a little too far forward, now a little too far back, or the tongue may be too high or too low, but his knowledge of the effect of each effort causes him to approach more and more closely to the exact position desired, till at last he gets it. The time spent in studying and representing the incorrect positions is not wasted, for it gives the pupil mastery over the instrument of speech itself, and the struggle to get exactitude of position with one difficult sound gives him power to get any other, just as the ability to hit one bull's eye qualifies a man to shoot at any mark.

I will now answer some of the questions that have been propounded to me.

The first question is: What is accent?

I have found in my past experience that accent is length. At least that we get a more natural effect from a deaf child if we give him the idea of making the accented syllable longer than the others rather than louder. The attempt to make the accented syllables louder often leads to a jerky utterance very unlike the effect we desire.

To make my meaning clear I will say that I do not think that we give a jerk of the abdominal muscles for every accented syllable, any more than the piper gives a jerk of the arm to mark the accented notes. The pressure upon the bag is continuous and the rhythm of the music is brought out by the differing durations of the notes. Of course the music may be made louder or softer by increasing or diminishing the pressure upon the bag, but this effect corresponds more to emphasis than to accent.

The fact that the effect of accent can be produced by lengthening the duration of a syllable, without any change in the loudness or volume of the voice may be demonstrated by a simple experiment.

Let a deaf child prolong the voice while you manipulate his lips so as to produce ƏIƏIƏIƏI, etc. (Mama, mama, etc.) Now, although he makes no variation in the loudness of his voice you can with your fingers produce the effect of accent by prolonging the syllable you desire to bring out. For example: If you prolong the open position you can make him say ƏIƏ] ƏIƏ], etc. (Mama, pronounced in the English way with the accent on the second syllable) or Ə]ƏI Ə]ƏI, etc., with the accent on the first syllable, as is very commonly heard in America.

"But," you may ask, "May not syllables containing short vowels be accented, and how can you prolong the syllable if the vowel is short?"

Certainly, syllables of this kind can be accented. In such cases you do not prolong the vowel but the succeeding consonant. For example: You can by manipulation cause your pupil to say ƏIƏ]Ə ƏIƏ]Ə, etc., (mamŭm, mamŭm, etc.), by prolonging the closed position of the lips instead of the open.

There is a great point here. Short vowels are succeeded by long consonants; for example: the consonant position is retained for a much longer time in such words as come, cuff, it, sin, look, than in such words as, calm, calf, eat, seen, Luke. You can demonstrate this prolongation of the consonant position by emphasizing with great force the word "not" in the familiar quotation, "To be, or NOT to be; that is the question." The hiatus caused by the prolongation of the shut position (Ʊ) of the *t* is so great as to occasion a perceptible silence in the midst of the sentence.

Let your pupils pronounce with precision the accented syllables of words and slur over the others, articulating them rapidly, with indefinite vowels, and the effect will be much more natural than a precise articulation of every syllable with loudness for accent.

MISS MCCOWEN: Have you ever thought of there being a difference in pitch?

DR. BELL: I don't see how that could come into the case. In natural speech the pitch of the voice is constantly varied in both accented and unaccented syllables. You can distinguish the element of accent even though the voice is on a monotone and without variation of loudness.

The next question on my list is: "Please imitate Helen Keller's voice."

I am sorry I have not a sufficiently distinct recollection to do that. Perhaps Miss Fuller can.

MISS FULLER: I don't think I can.

DR. BELL: I will say it was distinct and perfectly intelligible to persons not accustomed to the deaf.

The next question on my list is: "How would you teach *r* and *l*?"

I have experienced so little difficulty in teaching *r* and *l* (ω and ω) that I am inclined to think that the very defective manner in which these sounds are sometimes given by deaf children must be due to the mode of teaching. I always commence with the non-vocal forms ᴗ and ω. I would recommend you to adopt this plan generally in dealing with consonants as the non-vocal forms are usually more easily acquired than the others. It is especially advisable in the case of *r* and *l*, as you then avoid the common fault of too large aperture. When the non-vocal forms have been mastered, the vocal forms follow as a matter of course by the addition of voice

In forming ᴗ (non-vocal *r*) the point of the tongue is applied to the upper gum just at the part where the palate begins to arch, and the breath is allowed to escape through a central aperture. Deaf children acquire the sound very readily by imitation, as the whole mechanism can be seen in a mirror. In any case of difficulty I manipulate the sound from Ʊ (*th*) or Ʊ (*s*) in the manner described to you the other day. It is quite unnecessary to attempt a "trill" that is, to cause a vibration or trembling of the point of the tongue. Such an effect is un-English.

The defective variety of *r* most commonly met with results from placing the point of the tongue too far back in the mouth. For example: It is often applied to the top of the hard palate (ɷ$^{\cap}$); and in some cases it is coiled up within the mouth so as to approximate the soft palate (ɷ^{c}).

The defective form of *l* so common in schools for the deaf results from an exaggerated narrowing of the tongue (ωv) (too large aperture) and from opening the jaws too widely.

Sometimes the tip of the tongue is placed against the upper teeth and the under side of the tongue is actually protruded from the mouth.

The correct position for ω (*l*) is so nearly the same as that for ϖ (*n*) that the deaf have difficulty in distinguishing one from the other by the eye. This leads some children to substitute ϖ for ω (*n* for *l*).

In forming ω (*l*), the point of the tongue should be placed against the upper gum, and air allowed to escape through two side apertures. The lingual position for ϖ (*n*) is the same, excepting that the two side apertures are closed. Thus, the tongue appears slightly broader for ϖ (*n*) than for ω (*l*). The exaggerated narrowing of the tongue so commonly associated with *l* results in side apertures that are much too large. This defect is avoided, if you commence by teaching the sound non-vocally (ω) with quite small side apertures. Even pupils who give *n* for *l* readily acquire the non-vocal form (ω). After this has once been mastered, the vocal form follows as a matter of course by the addition of voice (ω).

Even though ɷ and ω (*r* and *l*) may be given correctly as elementary sounds, deaf children produce an effect that is not heard in ordinary utterance when they attempt to give these sounds after non-vocal consonants. Thus, Ʊɷʃ (tree), ΩωʃϽ> (sleep), etc., sound as if there were two syllables in each word, and if any defect of combination exist, the vocality of the *r* or *l* causes the introduction of a voice glide after the non-vocal consonant. Thus, ϖıɷʃ, Ωıωʃɔ> (tŭree, sŭleep), etc.

I have found that deaf children give the proper vernacular effect when they attempt to make the sounds non-vocally. Thus, ƆƱɭ, ƱωɭD> (tree, sleep). The same may be said of the sounds Ə and ൜ (*w* and *y*) after non-vocal consonants; for example, when deaf children attempt to say ƆƏ[ƱƆɭ, Ɑ൜ł (twenty, cue, *i. e.*, kyou), they are apt to give Ɔł[ƱƆɭ, Ɑɭł (too-enty, kee-oo), although the distinction between the consonant and vowel forms Ə–ł and ൜–ɭ (w-oo and y-ee) may have been fully explained to them. The vernacular effect, however, is at once produced when they try to give the sound non-vocally, Ɔ and ∩ (wh, yh). For example, ƆƆ[ƱƆɭ and Ɑ∩ł (twh-enty and k-hue). I would adopt the rule of teaching deaf children to give *r, l, w,* and *y* without voice (Ʊ, ω, Ɔ, and ∩), where they follow non-vocal consonants in the same syllable, for example, in such words as pry, try, cry, try, thrice, shrine; play clay, flay, slay; twin, queen, swim; pew, tune, cute, few, thews, sue.

Vocal consonants, when they occur as final elements, are pronounced by the deaf in such a manner as to offend the ordinary ear, and I think it worth while, therefore, to direct your attention to a simple expedient by which the effect may be much improved. For example:—take such words as love, nose, smooth, rub, good, bag, etc., when they occur by themselves or at the end of a phrase.

The vocality of the last element produces an effect that is at once recognized as peculiar. The effect is much improved when the pupil is taught to finish off with the non-vocal form of the consonant softly uttered. Thus ω]ƷƷ> (luvf) ƱłƱƱ> (noze) ƱƏłƱƱ> (smoodhth) ω]ƟD> (rubp) ƐłƱƆ> (goodt) Ɵ[ƐƆ> (bagk), etc.

When two vocal consonants end the last syllable uttered, it is better to give the last consonant non-vocally. Thus: [ƱΩ>, (edge), instead of [ƱΩ; (edsh, instead of edzh); Ʊ]ƷƱ>, instead of Ʊ]ƷƱ, (duvs instead of duvz), etc. When such words occur in the middle of a phrase the latter pronunciation is correct.

MISS BARTON: How do you get pupils to give long e easily?

DR. BELL: I always teach first the non-vocal form ∩ (*h* in *hue*). If a pupil does not give this readily, I manipulate it from Ʊ (*th*) or Ʊ (*s*) in the manner I have already described. When ∩ has been well fixed—that is, when a pupil can give it readily without manipulation, I add voice.

At once we get ɭ (*ee*) or, what is practically the same thing, ൜ (*y*).

The next question on my list is this:—

"Please demonstrate the teaching of *tn* in cotton."

In this word, (ɑɟʊɷ) the sound of *n* alone (ɷ) constitutes a distinct syllable. Indeed ʚ (*m*) ɷ (*n*) ɞ (*ng*) and also ω (*l*,) when prolonged, are in reality vowels. That is, the aperture through which the voice is passed is so large as to be non-obstructive. We fail to hear any rustling or hissing or puffing sound from the mouth position. The fricative noise which is characteristic of a consonant is not heard excepting at the moment of the relinquishment of the position. These sounds can be used both as consonants and vowels. If the positions are assumed only momentarily so that the sound of the removal of the position is the chief effect perceived, then we recognize the sounds as consonant elements of speech. If on the other hand the chief effect perceived is due to the retention of the position, and not to its removal, we hear only a quality of voice, that is, a vowel sound, and this sound may constitute a distinct syllable by itself.

In the English language ɷ (*n*) and ω (*l*) are often employed as vowels. ʚ (*m*) is more rarely used, ɞ (*ng*) not at all. A vowelized ʚ (*m*) is not usually recognized as constituting a distinct syllable by itself, but surely such words as ωʃʊʚ (rhythm) and ʊʃʊʚ (schism) are as really dis-syllabic as ʃʊɷ (eaten), ɑɟʊɷ (cotton), or ʈɒω (apple). The termination, "ful," which is so often murdered by deaf children is pronounced by most people simply as ɜω (fl). For example: ɟɜω (awfl), ʊωʈʊɜω (dreadful), ɞɱɪʊʃɜω (beautiful), etc. Surely the word ɟɜω (awfl) would be more acceptable to ordinary ears than the ɟɜıɘɨω pronunciation commonly heard from the deaf.

It is difficult to teach the sound of *tn* in such a word as cotton without the use of symbols. The pupil associates the single character *t* with a double action of the organs (ʊ>). Hence, he tries to give this double action to the *t* in cotton; that is, ʊ>ɷ for ʊɷ. The vocality of the ɷ (*n*), however, usually causes him to fail in his aim, so that the puff of air (>) is vocalized (ı). Thus, ɑɟʊıɷ. In our pronunciation of the word the point of the tongue is not removed from the upper gum between the positions for *t* and *n*, ɑɟʊɷ. The point-shut position is common to the two sounds ʊɷ. The soft palate is closed against the back of the pharynx (□) during the production of the *t* and drops (⊏) during the production of the *n* (see dotted lines in Figure 16), thus allowing the voice to pass through the nose.

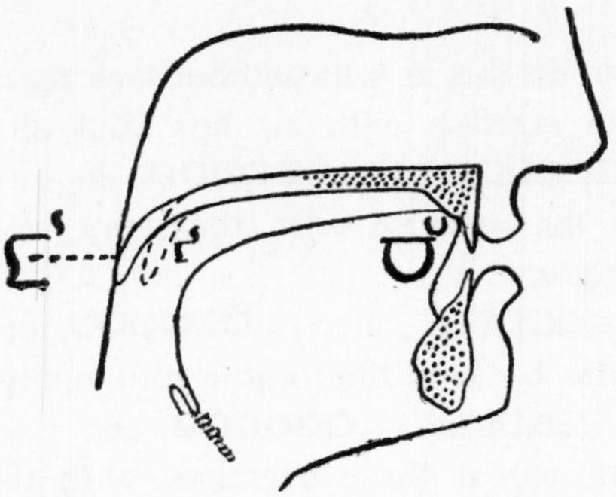

Fig. 16. Action of the soft palate in forming *tn* (ƱƱ̃) in "cotton."

First Position. □+Ʊ=Ʊ
Second Position. ⊏+Ʊ=Ʊ̃
Ʊ+(□⊏)=ƱƱ̃

Repeat the sound of *tn* a number of times without voice (ƱƱ̃ƱƱ̃ƱƱ̃, etc.), and you will feel that the whole action consists in the alternate elevation and depression of the soft palate [□⊏□⊏, etc]. The point of the tongue is not moved at all, but is shut continuously against the upper gum. ƱƱ̃ƱƱ̃ƱƱ̃=Ʊ+(□⊏□⊏□⊏, etc.).

There is only one point-shut position. Now, such an action presents no difficulty to a child who has been taught to elevate and depress his soft palate at will, but does present enormous difficulties to one who has not, for the whole action is invisible. All you can do in such a case is to use symbols, and show that the shut-position (Ʊ) of *t* (Ʊ>) is alone assumed, followed by Ʊ̃ (*n*) without moving the tongue. The combinations ƱƱ̃ (*tn*), Ʊ̃Ʊ> (*nt*), Ʊ̵Ʊ̃ (*dn*), Ʊ̃Ʊ̵> (*nd*), ƱƱ̃Ʊ> (*tnt*), and Ʊ̵Ʊ̃Ʊ̵> (*dnd*), occur in English words, some of them quite frequently; and I think therefore that deaf children should be taught to control the movement of the soft palate so as to be able to produce these combinations at will. For example: The words: ʃƱƱ̃ (eaten), ɩƱ̃Ʊ> (ant), ϶ɩƱ̵Ʊ̃ (madden), ɩƱ̃Ʊ̵> (and), Ɒɩ̃ƱƱ̃Ʊ> (patent), and ϶ɩƱ̵Ʊ̃Ʊ̵> (maddened), involve these actions.

The word "abandoned," as pronounced by some people ꞁƏɩƱ̃Ʊ̵Ʊ̃Ʊ̵> actually involves four point-shut sounds successively uttered, or rather one point-shut position, and four successive positions of the soft palate. Ʊ̃Ʊ̵Ʊ̃Ʊ̵=Ʊ̵+(⊏□⊏□>).

In difficult cases I would recommend the following plan: Give your pupil a hand mirror and teach him to elevate and depress his soft palate ([Visible Speech], etc.), in the manner described in my second lecture.

When he can do this at will without looking in the mirror, ask him to repeat the exercise with his lips shut all the time. This results in [Visible Speech]+([Visible Speech], etc.)=[Visible Speech], etc.

Then repeat the exercise with the point of the tongue shut against the upper gum:

[Visible Speech]+([Visible Speech], etc.,)=[Visible Speech], etc.

Then with the back of the tongue shut against the soft palate:

[Visible Speech]+([Visible Speech])=[Visible Speech], etc.

Then let him repeat these exercises with the voice sounded intermittently through the nose:

[Visible Speech], etc. (pm, pm, etc.)
[Visible Speech], etc. (tn, tn, etc.)
[Visible Speech], etc. (kng, kng, etc.)

Then with the voice continuously sounded:

[Visible Speech], etc. (bm, bm, etc.)
[Visible Speech], etc. (dn, dn, etc.)
[Visible Speech], etc. (gng, gng, etc.)

If a pupil is taught to control the movement of his soft palate at will, such combinations as that of *tn* in cotton will present no difficulty.

[Dr. Bell here illustrated his method with Mr. Kiesel].

CONSONANTS.

I propose in my lecture to-day to deal with the mechanism of speech. In my demonstrations I shall make use of Monroe's school-room charts, "Sounds Of The English Language," which contain good diagrams of the positions of the vocal organs in uttering English sounds. As you are professionally familiar with the subject it will be unnecessary for me to describe the correct positions unless in answer to questions. I shall therefore consider the mechanism of common defects. We shall consider first the defects of shut consonants.

DEFECTS OF SHUT CONSONANTS.

The labial letters, *p, b, m,* are not liable to errors of position. In forming *t, d, n,* slight changes of position do not offend the ordinary ear and may therefore be passed lightly by. The point of the tongue should be placed against the upper gum, but it may be shut against the teeth, even to the *th* position without producing a defect sufficient to attract the attention of any one but an articulation teacher. In forming *k, g, ng,* also, considerable latitude may be allowed so long as the position is too far forward. When it is too far back the defect at once attracts attention, and should be corrected. If you try to form a *k,* with your mouth opened as widely as possible, you will find it very difficult to raise the back of the tongue into contact with the soft palate. It is much more easy to produce the shutting action lower down by the approximation of the base of the tongue to the back of the pharynx. This produces the defective sound of *k* to which I have alluded (Ɑ‹), a sound quite commonly given by deaf children. I am inclined to think that the defect is due to the mode of teaching. The teacher is very apt to open her mouth as widely as possible to show her pupils the position of the tongue. They imitate the action, and this naturally leads them to give too low a position. It is very difficult to correct a position that is too far back. I think the best way is to teach the sound anew. Take a position which is too far forward, for example, *t* (Ʊ), then manipulate the tongue. The same remarks, of course, apply to *g* (ϵ).

The shut consonants, though generally pronounced well by deaf children, are liable to a defect of a very extraordinary nature. In nearly every school for the deaf some pupils may be found who give clicks in place of these consonants. For example: *p* will be pronounced like the sound of a kiss, and *t* like the clicking sound we make as a sign of impatience, or like the cluck with which we hurry up a horse. I may not be able to tell you exactly what to do, but of one thing you may be sure,—the first step in the correction of a defect is to understand the mechanism of the defective sound. "Knowledge is power," and when we know the nature of a defect, ingenuity will find a remedy.

The first step then is to study the mechanism of the defective sound. How are you to investigate it? Imitate the defective sound yourself, and then study your own vocal organs.

Your pupil, we shall suppose, gives a kiss instead of the sound of *p*. Let us study the mechanism together.

When the lips are opened you observe that air goes into the mouth instead of coming out. Let us examine into the cause.

But first, let us express by means of symbols and diagrams the condition of our knowledge at each stage of the investigation, so that we may realize as clearly as possible what we are about.

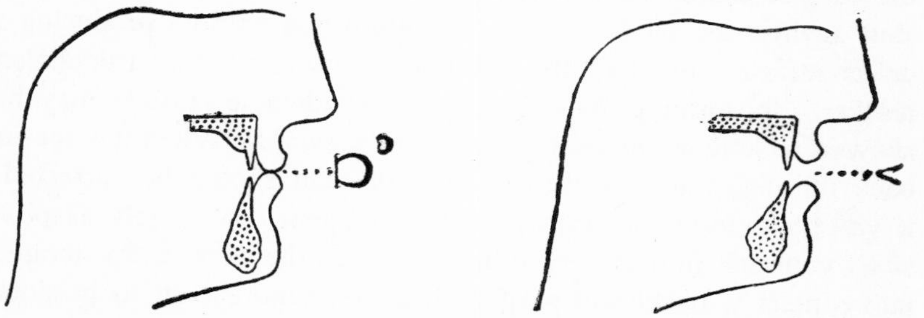

First Position. Fig. 11. Second Position.

D<

The first diagram in Fig. 11, illustrates the closure of the lips (D). The second shows, by means of an arrow-head, the direction of the air when the lips are opened (<).

Can it be that the pupil makes an effort of inspiration while he is trying to say *p*? How can we satisfy ourselves on this point?

Shut your lips then open them with an effort of inspiration. Thus, (D<). At once you notice that the effect is very different from the sound of a kiss. In forming the kiss, then, the air does not enter the lungs (<), but only goes into the mouth as far as some point [<] yet to be determined, [The symbol D< now becomes D<].

Repeat the kissing sound many times—D< D< D<, etc.,—while you observe what you do with your lungs. You will find that you can go on kissing for any length of time without stopping to take breath. You can breathe freely through the nose.

What conclusion can we draw from this? [1] The soft palate is depressed [ʃ].

[2] You can breathe freely through the nose thus showing that no constriction exists between the soft palate and the lungs.

Let us express this knowledge upon the diagrams we have made. Figure 11 now becomes Figure 12, and the symbol D< becomes ʃ + [D<].

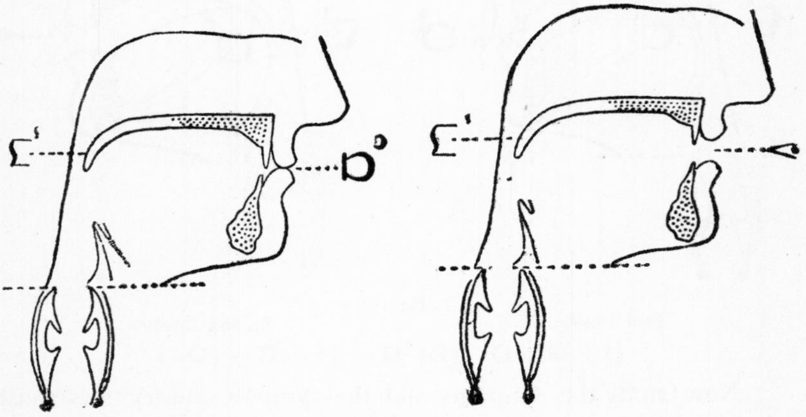

Fig. 12.

First Position. Second Position.

[ʃ+D] [ʃ+<]=ʃ[D<]

Is anything further to be discovered? Think for one moment. If no other constriction exists than is shown on the diagram, then there must be an open passage-way into the mouth from the lungs, and air should escape through the mouth as well as through the nose. Does it do so? We know it does not, for when the lips are opened air enters the mouth in just the opposite direction [< and not >]. The passage-way, then, must be closed somewhere between the soft palate and the lips. What organs are there in the mouth by which the closure could be effected? We are limited in our choice to the point of the tongue, the "top" or "front" of the tongue, the back of the tongue, or to intermediate parts.

If you repeat the sound of a kiss, I think you will feel that the concealed shut position must be pretty far back in the mouth. Certainly the point of the tongue is not involved, and we are limited therefore, to the top or back of the tongue, with the probabilities in favor of the back. How can you decide the matter? Make a hypothesis, and then experiment upon your mouth to test the truth of your assumption. For example: Assume that the back of the tongue is shut against the soft palate (ɑ). Fill in this position upon the diagrams. Figure 12 now becomes Figure 13, and the expression ʃ + (D<) becomes ʚ + (D<)

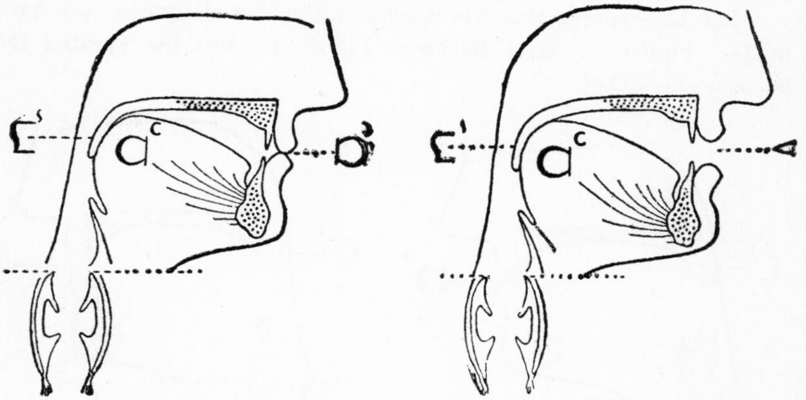

Fig. 13.

First Position. Second Position.

(ʃ + ɑ + D) (ʃ + ɑ + <) = ʚ + (D<)

Now study the diagrams and the symbols and try to establish some relation between the hypothetical position (ʚ) and some sound of known formation. Then experiment upon the mouth to see if that relation holds good.

Now we know that ʚ + I = ɞ (*ng*).

If then your hypothetical position (ʚ) is correct, you should get ɞ (*ng*), by adding voice to a kiss. Test the matter. Sound the voice continuously while you repeat the sound of a kiss:—

I + ʚ + (D< D< D< etc.) = ɞ + (D< D< D< etc).

You at once recognize the familiar effect ɞ (*ng*), continuously sounded—like the drone of a bagpipe—accompanied by the equally familiar sound of kissing. This is proof that your assumption is correct.

A kiss $=$ $\mathcal{G}+(D\prec)$.

The defect, then, consists in the assumption of the *ng* position
without voice (\mathcal{G}) while the pupil is trying to say $D>$ (p).

But why does the air go into the mouth when the lips are
opened ? The fact indicates that a partial vacuum exists there. This
means that the cavity of the mouth had been enlarged while the
shut positions were assumed, thus causing rarefaction of the contained air. The tongue, therefore, must have been moved before

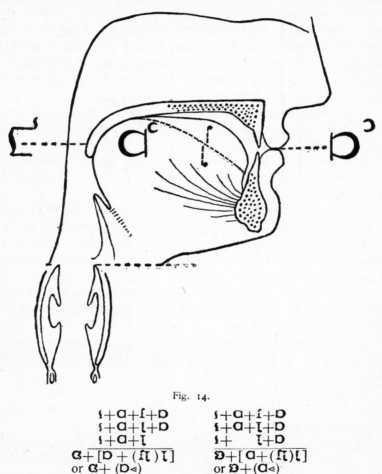

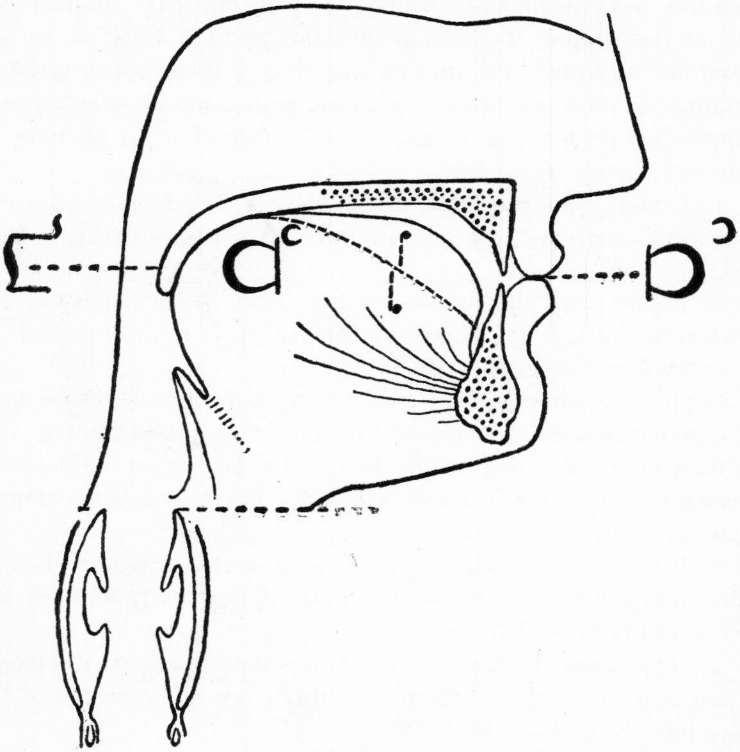

Fig. 14.

$$\begin{array}{cc} \mathfrak{s}+\mathfrak{a}+\mathfrak{f}+D & \mathfrak{s}+\mathfrak{a}+\mathfrak{f}+D \\ \mathfrak{s}+\mathfrak{a}+\mathfrak{l}+D & \mathfrak{s}+\mathfrak{a}+\mathfrak{l}+D \\ \mathfrak{s}+\mathfrak{a}+\mathfrak{l} & \mathfrak{s}+\quad\mathfrak{l}+D \\ \mathcal{G}+[D+(\mathfrak{fl})\mathfrak{l}] & \mathfrak{D}+[\mathfrak{a}+(\mathfrak{fl})\mathfrak{l}] \\ \text{or } \mathcal{G}+(D\prec) & \text{or } \mathfrak{D}+(\mathfrak{a}\prec) \end{array}$$

the lips were opened. Any movement of the tongue that will enlarge the cavity, will produce a partial vacuum in the mouth, and
thus lead to the production of the sound. The symbol \prec (air going
into a cavity) expresses the effect independently of the exact

positions assumed. Hence: G + (D<), is a general expression and covers any change of position inside the mouth that will produce a partial vacuum there.

As a clear understanding of the cause of the click effect in this case will throw light upon the nature of clicks in general, it may be well to show some specific movement of the tongue that will produce the effect. For example: Suppose that the front of the tongue is elevated in the position for *e* in *eel* thus ſ (high front) when the shut positions are assumed. (See Fig. 14). If then the front of the tongue is lowered into the position for *e* in *pet* (as shown by a dotted line in Fig. 14) thus ʈ (low front), without changing the other positions, the cavity of the mouth is enlarged. As a partial vacuum then exists, air will rush in if an opening is made anywhere. For example:—

1. If you keep the back of the tongue closed against the soft palate and open the lips, air will rush in between the lips; G + (D<).

2. If you keep the lips closed and open the passage-way be-between the back of the tongue and the soft palate, air will rush in the cavity from behind Ɔ + (ɑ<).

Suppose again that instead of starting with the tongue elevated you commence with it depressed ʈ (as shown by dotted line Fig. 14,) and then elevate the tongue into the position for *e* in *eel* ſ, the cavity between the two shut positions is reduced in size and the contained air compressed. Then:—

3. If you keep the back of the tongue closed against the soft palate and open the lips, air will rush out of the cavity through the labial aperture G + (D>); or

4. If you keep the lips closed and open the passage-way between the back of the tongue and the soft palate, air will rush out of the cavity into the pharynx Ɔ + (ɑ>).

Numbers 1 and 2 are suction clicks. Numbers 3 and 4 are expulsion clicks. Numbers 1 and 3 are both given by deaf children instead of *p* (D>).

In order to have a click sound it is necessary that you should have a cavity in which the air is of different density from that outside. There must, therefore, be two constrictions of the passage-way which we may call *x*, *y*, with a cavity between them. If the air in that cavity is of less density than the air outside, the opening of the passage-way at either end will result in a sudden in-rush of air, forming a suction click.

It the air in the cavity is of greater density, an expulsion click will be produced. Double positions are, therefore, capable of producing two suction clicks, and two expulsion clicks which may be thus symbolized:—

1. $x + (y⋖)$ } *Suction Clicks.*
2. $y + (x⋖)$ }

3. $x + (y⋗)$ } *Expulsion Clicks.*
4. $y + (x⋗)$ }

In my use of the symbols—

\> means air going out from the lungs;

< means air going into the lungs;

⋗ means air going out from a cavity;

⋖ means air going into a cavity.

I have alluded to two labial clicks made by deaf children instead of P. There is still a third which is quite common Ꭓ + (D⋗).

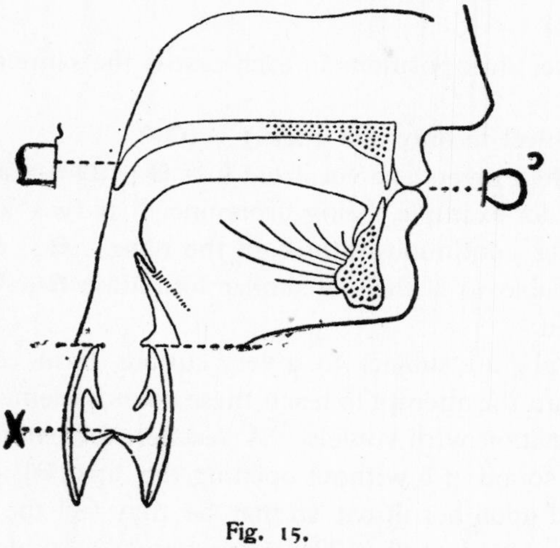

Fig. 15.

1. Ꭓ + ◻ + (D⋖) } *Suction Clicks.*
2. Ꭓ + (◻⋖) + D }
3. (Ꭓ⋖) + ◻ + D }

4. Ꭓ + ◻ + (D⋗) } *Expulsion Clicks.*
5. Ꭓ + (◻⋗) + D }
6. (Ꭓ⋗) + ◻ + D }

The inner shut position is produced by the closure of the glottis (Ꭓ) (See Fig. 15), and the cavity between the two shut positions is larger than in the case shown in Fig. 14. The sound therefore has a lower pitch than any of the clicks resulting from the positions shown in Fig. 14.

The pupil also is unable to breathe through the nose while producing the sound.

The closure of the soft palate against the back ot the pharynx (ꓷ) is of course assumed though not expressed in the symbol X + (D>). There are really in this case three shut positions, and theory therefore indicates the possibility of producing three expulsion and three suction clicks from the positions shown. Below Fig. 15 I give the symbols for the six clicks alluded to for the benefit of those who desire to study them. I need not describe them further in detail, as we meet with only one of them—the fourth—in our work.

The fourth click X + (D>) is sometimes given by deaf children in place of D> (*p*).

We meet with three click forms of Ʊ> (*t*), ɞ+(Ʊ<); ɞ+ (Ʊ>); and X + (Ʊ>)

The inner shut positions in each case is the same as that already noted for *p*.

K is subject to only one click X + (Ɑ>).

M is often given as a vocalized kiss Ɛ+ (D<)—such a word as "mamma" for example, being pronounced as two kisses with the voice passing continuously through the nose. Ɛ+ (D<D<).

N is liable to a click of similar formation Ɛ+(Ʊ<), but *ng* is never clicked.

B, *d* and *g* are subject to a very curious form of suction click resulting from the attempt to teach these sounds elementarily instead of in combination with vowels. A teacher, for example, will pronounce the sound of *b* without opening the lips (ʚ), and place her pupil's hand upon her throat so that he may feel the vibration produced by the vocal cords. The voice cannot be prolonged because the closure of the lips prevents the escape of air. The pupil therefore feels only a momentary impulse of voice; and in attempting to imitate this effect, he makes a sudden muscular effort.

If you place your hand upon the pupil's throat while he makes the sound, you will observe a strong muscular effort causing an expansion of the whole throat. The cavity between the vocal cords and the lips is thus enlarged, creating a partial vacuum within. The slit-like aperture of the glottis is not large enough to permit air to freely enter the cavity from the lungs so as to restore the pressure.

Upon opening the lips, therefore, air enters the cavity from outside, thus forming a suction click, I + (D<).

D and *g* are liable to a similar defect. For example: *d* = I + (Ʊ<), *g* = I + (ɑ<). These clicks, unfortunately, are of very common occurrence.

TABLE OF CLICKS GIVEN BY DEAF CHILDREN.

For *p*.	ʚ + (D<)	ʚ + (D>)	)(+ (D>)
For *t*.	ʚ + (Ʊ<)	ʚ + (Ʊ>)	)(+ (Ʊ>)
For *k*.	———	———	)(+ (ɑ>)
For *m*.	ɞ + (D<)	———	———
For *n*.	ɞ + (Ʊ<)	———	———
For *ng*.	———	———	———
For *b*.	———	———	I + (D<)
For *d*.	———	———	I + (Ʊ<)
For *g*.	———	———	I + (ɑ<)

If you have followed me so far, you will recognize the fact that clicks result from double positions of the vocal organs. When, therefore, you hear a click, you know that there is a constriction somewhere which is concealed from direct observation. In studying the defect, therefore, your first object should be to discover where that concealed position is. The clicks most commonly given by deaf children result either from the closure of the back of the tongue against the soft palate (ɑ), or from the closure of the glottis ( )( ).

If the pupil can breathe through the nose, you may assume at once that the concealed position is ʚ (*ng*, without voice). If he does not breathe through the nose, the location is more uncertain (either ɑ or)( ). The pitch of the sound may help you here, for a click which is due to the closure of the glottis is lower in pitch than one due to the closure of the back of the tongue against the soft palate, because the cavity is larger. Perhaps the most certain plan of ascertaining the location is to cause the pupil to repeat the click for as long a time as possible without stopping.

If he is not breathing through the nose, nature will sooner or later force him to relinquish the concealed position in order to take breath. Watch for that moment. At the moment of relinquishment a sound will be heard which will enable you to determine by ear the location of the concealed position. For example: If the back of the tongue is involved you will hear the sound of *k* (ɑ< or ɑ>), pronounced either with the air going in or out of the lungs. If the glottis is closed you will hear ()(> or)(<) the effect of throat shut followed by a puff of air. If you are uncertain whether or not the pupil can breathe through the nose, hold the nostrils closed with your fingers until the pupil's breath gives out. If the concealed position was Ꞓ (*ng* without voice) you should hear the sound of *k* (ɑ> or ɑ<) for Ꞓ — ʃ = ɑ.

The first step in the correction of a defect is a knowledge of the cause. With this knowledge the teacher can not only devise means (1) of correcting the defect, but (2) of utilizing it in the production of other sounds. Let us take as a typical case of a click defect, the sound of a kiss given instead of *p*. How can we correct it and how can we utilize it?

(1) *Correction of the defect.* In this case the cause consists in the assumption of a shut position (Ꞓ) which prevents the breath from reaching the lips. If then, we can devise any method of causing air from the lungs to press against the lips the assumption of the concealed position becomes impossible. For example: You can make your pupil blow feathers or pieces of paper away from his lips, or inflate his cheeks while trying to pronounce *p*.

These are simple expedients that are usually successful; but they may fail because it is perfectly possible to produce inflation of the cheeks and expulsion of air from the mouth, and yet have the back of the tongue shut against the soft palate when the lips are opened.

The characteristic puff heard during the production of a click is necessarily of very short duration. Then get your pupil to make a continuous effort of expiration. For example: Let him shut his lips and blow continuously through a very fine orifice between them (DƆ+) as though he were blowing to cool something.

In producing a prolonged emission of this kind the air can only come from the lungs, and the assumption of any interior shut position is therefore impossible. It is true that the inflation of the cheeks suggested above, and the too small aperture between the lips just alluded to, themselves constitute defects; but they are easily corrected, because the actions are visible. A skillful teacher will not hesitate to substitute a defect that is easy of correction for one that is more difficult.

(2) *Utilization of the defective sound.* The moment you realize that the concealed shut position is Ɑ you will recognize the possibility of producing *ng* (Ɛ) from a kiss. For example: Get the pupil to add voice to the kiss.

[Ɑ+ (Ɔ<)] +I=Ɛ+(Ɔ<)

and at once you obtain *ng* combined with a labial action. By manipulation of the pupil's mouth you can prevent the lips from closing,

[Ɛ+ (Ɔ<)] – (Ɔ<) =Ɛ

and you then get *ng* alone. If the pupil has not already acquired the sound of *ng*, you can thus utilize the kiss as a means of teaching it to him; and if he already has the sound and knows its symbol (Ɛ) then the presentation of the symbol for the kiss will convey to his mind an idea of the mechanism of the click. In correcting defects, it is surely advisable, if possible, that the pupil as well as the teacher should know the cause and understand the mechanism of the defective sound.

If then your little pupil should happen to give the sound of a kiss instead of the letter *p*, don't frown at him and say, "No, no, that is not right." Give him the symbol Ɑ+ (Ɔ<) and encourage him by a sign of approval.

He has tried his best and it is not his fault that he failed to give the sound you wanted. All sounds are but positions to him and he was right in his attempt—not wrong—for he imitated correctly the position which alone he could see—the position of the lips. Why then should we express disapproval? He had done nothing worthy of censure. The "No–no method" does not help him to correct the defect—and it does throw cold water upon honest attempts to please. Give him a sign for his sound, and reward his effort by approbation. If you do not know how to write the sound properly give him *x* as a provisional symbol—or invent a character to represent it. Say, "That is what you did, now do it again." The "No–no method" gives him the idea that it is wrong to make a noise of that kind. On the contrary, encourage him to repeat the sound so that you may study it and find out how best to utilize it in his instruction. If the sound is unfamiliar to your ear and you do not know how it is formed, that itself is a reason why you should hold on to it and not throw it away. When you have analyzed its composition you may find it to contain gold where you only asked for lead. Let your pupil repeat the sound until you can imitate it yourself. Then study your own mouth. In the meantime do not let him forget the sound. Fix it by reference to the letter *x*, or some other mark, and when you have satisfied yourself how it should be expressed, substitute for *x* the proper symbol.

The meaning of the symbol need not be explained to a young child. It may be treated as an arbitrary sign. The expression Ꞓ+(D<) need only mean to him, "That's what you did, now do it again." The deaf child soon comes to understand the application of the symbols even though he may not understand their full meaning. For example: When he knows that Ꞓ+(D<) represents the sound he makes, then if you change the symbol to Ɛ+(D<) he will at once attempt to vocalize the kiss. He will do this even though he may be unable to analyze or understand the full significance of the expression.

The symbols of Visible Speech are invaluable as a means of correcting and utilizing defective sounds. Indeed, I think their chief value lies in their ability to express the mechanism of the sounds the children make, so as to show in a graphical manner their relation to the English sounds we wish them to give.

The methods suggested above are applicable to the correction of all the clicks of *t* and *k*. (See Table of Clicks).

DEFECTIVE COMBINATIONS OF *P, T, K.*

Pupils who are taught by means of Visible Speech have many advantages over those taught only by means of Roman letters and diacritical marks. Defects of combination, which are inevitable upon the latter plan, and which require the expenditure of much time and labor on the part of the teacher in order to correct them, need not arise at all when symbols are employed, and if they do arise are easily corrected.

Let me illustrate by a common case.

The position for *p* (D) by itself yields no sound, because the lips are closed. It is usual, therefore, to teach it in combination with an open position. Thus, D>. The lips are first shut and then opened to allow of the escape of a puff of air.

Here we have two successive positions represented by only one character *p*. This leads at once to a defect when *p* is combined with other letters, for the child naturally attempts to give both positions (D>) wherever *p* occurs. Thus, *ps* becomes D>℧ instead of D℧ (a puff of air appears between the *p* and *s*). So also with *t* and *k*.

Ts becomes U>℧ instead of U℧.
Ks becomes ɑ>℧ instead of ɑ℧.
Tsh(*ch*) becomes U>Ω instead of UΩ, etc.

These defects are inevitable upon the Roman letter plan. Without the use of symbols it is difficult to explain the nature of the defect to a deaf child who knows no language. The teacher usually imitates the defective sound and exclaims, "Don't say U>Ω, but UΩ (tsh)," trusting to the quickness of the pupil's eye to discern the difference in her mouth. Your chief reliance is upon imitation, and if that fails you, where are you? Now, these defects need not arise at all when the sounds are taught by symbols; and when they do occur, they are easily corrected, because we can express the incorrect as well as the correct effect so as to exhibit the difference.

In teaching these sounds by means of visible speech we commence in the same way as that just described—by teaching *p, t* and *k,* as D>, U>, and ɑ> but we employ two characters to express the two positions instead of one. Then when the sound of *s* (℧)is acquired we combine as follows:

1. "Say U>" "That is right."
2. "Now say ℧" "Right."
3. "Now say U>℧" "Right again."

(Observe the difference in the attitude of the teacher towards her pupil. Here is the very defective combination of *ts* alluded to above. But the teacher of visible speech, having expressed the positions actually assumed by her pupil, can truthfully say, "That's right," with an approving nod--where the Roman letter teacher could only say, "No, no, that's wrong.")

4. "Now try first U>℧ and then U℧."

Here the pupil's attention is directed to the *difference* between the two effects, and his aim is to give the last combination *without the puff af air* (>). Whatever he does, therefore, his aim is right—which is not the case on the Roman letter plan. And whatever he does, the teacher can give him a symbol for his sound and say, "That's what you did, now do it again."

In a little time quite a number of variations upon the sound of *ts* may be obtained. Anxiety to avoid the puff of air often leads him to put it in—now in one place, now in another; for example, the pupil may say, Ʊ>Ʊ or >ƱƱ or >Ʊ>Ʊ, etc.

It is not the teacher's object to have him *forget* the incorrect sounds but to *remember* them and contrast them one with the other. The greater the number of slight variations that can be pronounced at will by the pupil the more power does he obtain over his vocal organs. A good marksman should be able to hit one mark just as well as another.

The sound of *ch* (tsh) presents exceptional difficulties to a deaf child. Even when the *t* is properly combined with *sh* without any puff of air between the two (thus ƱΩ) your ear usually tells you that there is something wrong when the combination is uttered in a word.

I think the fault lies in the undue prolongation of the *sh* position (ƱΩ+). If you observe your own utterance of such words as chair, cheese, church, such, much, touch, watch, etc., you will notice that the tongue does not remain for any length of time in the *sh* position. The *sh* indeed constitutes a non-vocal glide, a mere transitional effect, between *t* and the succeeding element. The unnatural effect produced by prolongation is most marked when *sh* occurs finally, as in much, touch, etc. (Ə]ƱΩ+ Ʊ]ƱΩ+, etc.). I have rarely failed to obtain the vernacular effect from a deaf child by expressing the sound of *ch* final as ƱΩ> instead of ƱΩ. Indeed, as a general rule a non-vocal consonant occurring as a final element is most naturally given by a deaf child when the symbol for the sound is followed by >. For example:

(cuff) Ɑ]Ʒ>	(us)]Ʊ>	(both) ƏʄƱ>	(wish) ƏʃΩ>
(cup) Ɑ]Ɒ>	(nut) Ʊ]Ʊ>	(sick) ƱʃƱ>	(maps) Ə[ƊƱ>
(cuffs) Ɑ]ƷƱ>	(nuts) Ʊ]ƱƱ>	(deaths) Ʊ[ƱƱ>	(books) ƏłƱƱ>
(watch) ƏʄƱΩ>			

Of course, when these words occur in the middle of a phrase, the puff of air must be omitted, for the phrase is pronounced as one word and the consonant is then no longer final.

CORRECTION OF THE DEFECTS OF *B*, *D*, *G*, *M* AND *N*.

It is difficult to pronounce the sound of *b* (Ə), without opening the lips and when a deaf child attempts to do this a defective sound arises which, when combined in a word with other sounds, produces the click form of *b* [I+(D<)] alluded to in the table of clicks. *D* and *g* are subject to a similar defect.

I would recommend combining these consonants with vowels from the very first. I commence with an indefinite vowel (I), which may be *er* her, *u* in up, or any indefinite vowel sound that the child can make. For example: *B, d, g* may be taught as ƏI ƱI ɘI (ber, der, ger, or bŭ, dŭ, gŭ, etc.) There is really no difficulty in teaching *b* in combination, for it can be manipulated while the child produces the vowel sound. Let the child prolong an indefinite vowel sound with his lips pretty close together. Now place your thumb and finger under his lower lip and move the lip rapidly up and down so as to close and open the labial aperture. This results in ƏIƏIƏI etc. (ber, ber, ber, etc.) Care should be taken to make the movement an opening not a closing action. The closure should be only momentary. The under lip should instantly rebound from the upper lip as a hammer rebounds from an anvil. Now teach the child himself to move his lip up and down with his finger. His attempt should be to pronounce the vowel (I) continuously and make no muscular effort with the lips. After he can do this well let him try to move his lip rapidly up and down in the same way without the assistance of his hand. There should be no muscular tension, but on the contrary the lips should feel soft and loose.

You cannot manipulate the point of the tongue in this way, but when the pupil can pronounce ƏIƏIƏI, etc., analogy leads him to give ƱIƱIƱI etc., (der der der, etc.) and ɘIɘIɘI etc., (*gŭ gŭ gŭ* etc.)

The clicks of *m* and *n* are more difficult of correction. After the child can give ƏIƏIƏI etc., or ƱIƱIƱI etc., it is well to try whether analogy will not lead him to give ƏIƏIƏI or ƱIƱIƱI etc. This often succeeds, but in difficult cases the back of the tongue remains closed against the soft palate, thus converting the sound into ɘ+(D<D<D<) or ɘ+(Ʊ<Ʊ<Ʊ< etc.) a continuous sound of *ng* accompanied by a succession of clicks. The defect is due to the retention of the back-shut position (Ɑ). I think, therefore, the best way to deal with a difficult case is to aim at control of the back of the tongue, so that the pupil shall acquire the power of elevating and depressing it at will. I would suggest taking the concealed position ɘ by itself and combining this with an indefinite vowel sound thus: ɘIɘIɘI etc.

When he can do this well contrast it with ƏIƏIƏI etc., thus ɘIɘIɘI ƏIƏIƏI etc., ɘIƏIɘIƏI etc. The analogy of the symbols will probably lead him to give the correct effect.

Wh and *w* (Ɔ and Ə) are very defectively given by deaf children, but I have already spoken of the mode of correction in a former lecture.

F, *v*, *th*, ŧh, (3 3 ʊ ω) present no difficulties of importance. S, *sh*, *yh*, (Ʊ Ω ∩) and their vocal forms *Z*, *zh*, *y* (ω Ω and ⋒), are liable chiefly to faults of position. That is, the tongue may be a little too far forward (›); or too far back (‹); or too high up. There may be too much compression of the passage-way (∧); or too little compression (∨).

My plan of correction is—to write what the pupil does, using these modifiers according to the character of the defect to be symbolized. For example: Ω‹ Ω› Ω∨ Ω∧ etc.

I then get the pupil to vary the position slightly and contrast the new position with the old making him pronounce both sounds alternately so as to observe their difference.

In difficult cases it is well to manipulate the non-vocal forms *s*, *sh*, and *yh*, (Ʊ, Ω, and ∩,) from *th* (ʊ) in the manner I have already described in answer to a question. When these are well fixed the vocal forms follow as a matter of course by the addition of voice.

VOWELS, GLIDES, AND COMBINATIONS.

DR. A. GRAHAM BELL: I have advocated the very general use of an indefinite, in place of a definite vowel sound in unaccented syllables. You must not, however, suppose from this that I undervalue vowels, or deem accuracy of vowel quality of no practical importance in our work. Far from it. I only mean to insist that vowels are of secondary importance to consonants.

Consonants give intelligibility to speech, but vowels give beauty of utterance. Consonants constitute the back-bone of spoken language—vowels the flesh and blood. You cannot do without them.

We want our pupils to acquire, not merely an intelligible articulation, but also, if possible, a natural and pleasant quality of speech. We must, therefore, attend to the vowels. It is neither necessary, however, nor advisable, that every vowel in a phrase should be given its full value. Unaccented syllables should be toned down like the shaded portions of a picture thus bringing out by contrast, the accented parts of words.

Beauty of utterance depends as much upon shading as upon form—as much upon the due subordination of the unaccented syllables as upon accuracy of vowel quality.

It is a very difficult thing, even for hearing persons, to give unaccented vowels their proper sounds without bringing them out too prominently, so as to produce that pedantic style of pronunciation which is often mistaken for elocution.

The really good speaker gives the proper value to unaccented vowels without italicizing them to the ear. The mass of the deaf, however, are no more able to do this, than the mass of the hearing. Indeed, the attempt results in a much more unnatural effect than the utterance of the pedantic speaker—because the vowel quality itself is usually defective. Under such circumstances indefiniteness is of importance. It produces, not a worse, but a better effect. You must not suppose, when I advocate a careless utterance of unaccented syllables, that I am urging you to teach worse speech than your pupils now possess; on the contrary, I believe that the result will be recognized as a great improvement. You will tone down sounds that are usually defective so that they will not come out so prominently to the ear; and accent, which is now conspicuous chiefly by its absence, will be produced by the subordination of the unimportant parts of words.

Give as definite vowels as possible in the accented syllables, but don't be too precise about the others.

Vowels are the most difficult elements we are called upon to teach. Why is this so? The discovery of the cause may perhaps enable us to devise a remedy. Let us examine into the matter.

How do vowel positions differ from the positions that yield consonant sounds? They result from larger apertures. Can this have anything to do with the difficulty of the acquirement? It seems so, for wide-aperture vowels are more difficult to obtain in perfection than the others.

Get a pupil to prolong a small-aperture vowel. The sound, even when defective, has a definite quality of its own. A lower position of the tongue, however, yields an effect of indefinite kind. The oral aperture is usually too large and the sound, when prolonged, is unstable and variable in quality, showing that the pupil finds difficulty in retaining the position unchanged.

Sometimes the attempt results in a visible trembling of the tongue.

In forming consonants and small-aperture vowels, the tongue makes actual contact with the upper part of the mouth at one or more points; but in lower positions it is hung in the air, so to speak, without anything against which to press. Extend your arm and you can easily retain it in a fixed position if you press your hand against the under surface of a table or shelf, but extend it in the air and I fancy you will find more difficulty in keeping it still. Your hand—if you do not watch it—is apt to waver like the unsteady tongue of the deaf child, and a constant tendency exists to a lower position.

Your ear aids you in the retention of a vowel position, because any change affects the quality of the sound.

Try to keep your tongue still, without making any noise, and you will appreciate the difficulty experienced by your pupil. He lacks a guide.

Give him a mirror and at once he becomes conscious of the movement of his tongue.

The sound is your guide, and if you merely think of the sound, that helps you to retain the position. His guide must be sight, and by seeing he will learn control. The thought of the image he has seen in the mirror will help him, as the thought of the sound helps you.

I cannot overestimate the value and importance of a mirror in articulation work. It is not enough that a pupil should watch his teacher's mouth, he must see his own. Accuracy and definiteness of sound depend upon the ability to retain a position unchanged. Indeed, as I said in my second lecture, control over the vocal organs is gained not so much by moving them as by keeping them still. Clearness of pronunciation depends upon the ability to enunciate every element in a word with clearness and deliberation. A poor speaker finds difficulty in uttering a word slowly or separating it into its component parts.

Give your pupil a mirror and let him learn to keep his tongue still. It doesn't much matter what he does, so long as he assumes different positions of the tongue, retaining each for some time without motion.

Little children delight to puzzle one another by assuming unusual positions of the tongue which the others cannot imitate. They should be encouraged in this, for all exercises of that kind are of value as a preparation for speech. By such exercises they unconsciously gain control over their vocal organs and become better able to imitate positions of the mouth. They feel a certain muscular exertion and see the effect in the mirror, and this constant association of seeing and feeling ultimately enables them to realize by muscular sensation alone exactly what the tongue is doing.

I consider a looking glass as a necessity in the schoolroom. You can no more expect to teach a deaf child good speech without a mirror than you can hope to teach a hearing child to paint well without letting him see the result of his efforts.

I would especially recommend as an exercise before a mirror alternately narrowing and broadening the tongue. The attempt to narrow the tongue causes it to become stiff and hard to the touch, with a rounded surface. When it is broadened the surface becomes flat and soft. The most common fault, I think, among deaf children is an exaggerated muscular action leading to a stiffening and narrowing of the tongue. For example: Many children in trying to form ſ (*ee*) make so much muscular effort that the tongue feels hard. The tongue is narrowed and fits up into the arch of the palate, making contact with the top of the hard palate, and though a centre aperture exists over the front of the tongue the effect of the vowel ſ is not produced. I have found C (the German *ch*) to be a very important position. It forms, indeed, the key note to the vowels. As a general rule if a child can pronounce C you can teach him to glide the tongue forward (C›) and backward (C‹), retaining the small centre aperture, and by getting him to do this as far back and as far forward as possible, the latter position generally gives ∩, which, by the addition of voice, becomes a good ſ (*ee*). In difficult cases I have found it a good plan to give the pupil the idea that ∩ is C modified by expansion of the tongue so as to press sideways against the molar teeth on each side instead of pressing up into the arch of the palate. In some cases the simple direction to broaden the tongue will correct the defective ſ (*ee*).

Pupils sometimes give I or even l for ſ (*ee*), and sometimes ſ I or l. These defects arise from the attempt to say *ee* with the teeth too far apart. You cannot pronounce (*ee*) properly with the mouth wide open. A teacher, however, is apt to separate the teeth as much as possible in order to show her pupil the position of the tongue. The pupil imitates the opening of the jaws, and this is apt to result in a position of the tongue too far back (I or l) or in a position having too wide an aperture (ſI or l).

I give below a tabulated list of the elementary vowels used in the English language arranged in such a manner as to show their place in the complete vowel scheme elaborated by my father.

MELVILLE BELL'S VOWEL SCHEME.

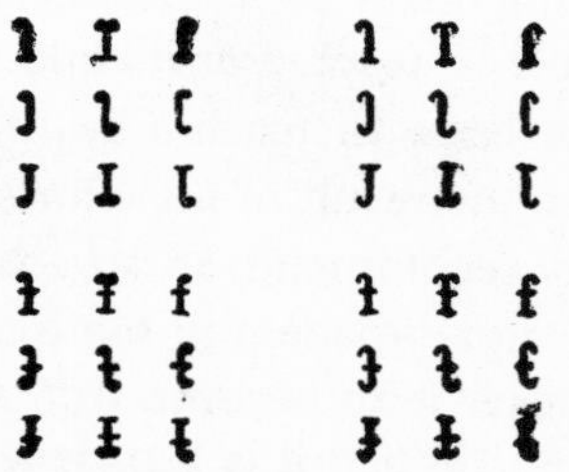

ENGLISH VOWELS.

—	—	ſ	—	—	ſ
]	—	[]	ι	—
—	—	ι	J	I	ι
ʇ	—	—	ʇ	—	—
ʒ	—	—	—	—	—
ʒ	—	—	ʒ	—	—

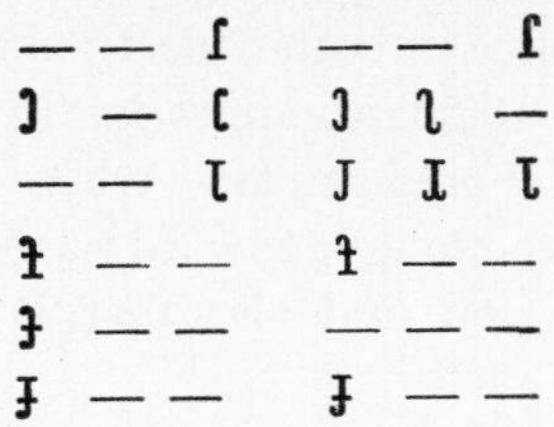

Some one has observed that you may at any time produce a Scotch air by striking at random the black notes of the piano. The musical scale of the Celts is defective. Examine the gamut of vowel sounds as given by my father, and you will notice that the English ear seems to be as defective for vowel sounds as the Scotch ear is for musical notes. Only three of the back series of vowels are used in the English language; two of the mixed series, and five of the front series. Out of the eighteen round vowels, only five in all are employed in our language.

You will observe a curious likeness between the peculiarities of the "front" and "back-round" series of vowels. The first one of each series (ſ and ʇ) is always of long duration in English, and the second (ſ and ʇ) always short. The third ([and ʒ) never occurs by itself, but is used simply as the initial part of a diphthong. The sound ends with the gliding of the tongue to the high vowel of its series. Thus [is pronounced as ſ (*ā*), finishing off with the gliding of the tongue towards the position for ſ (*ee*); and ʒ(*oh*) is given as ʒʇ, finishing off with a glide towards the position for ʇ (*ōō*.) The fourth vowel of each series is wanting in English. The fifth vowel of the front series ι (*e* in *pet*) is sometimes long and sometimes short. The fifth of the back-round series, however, ʒ (*aw*) is always long. In both series the sixth vowel (ʒ or ι) is always of short duration.

It may also be noted that the mid-back vowel] (*u* in *up*) also is always short.

These peculiarities of duration do not necessarily pertain to the vowels, but are mere matters of English usage. Many persons have the mistaken idea that the vowels in the words *eat*, and *it; pool* and *pull; caught* and *cot; calm* and *come*, are the long and short forms of the same vowels, but if you sing these words you will recognize that the vowels remain distinct to the ear when equally prolonged; and you can shorten the vowels in the words *eat, pool, caught* and *calm*, without producing *it, pull, cot* and *come*. In fact, this is the pronunciation given for these words by French speakers of English.

I am inclined to think that there is some natural cause for the analogous peculiarities appearing in the front and back-round series of vowels, because I notice in both dialectic and individual utterance that variations from the standard, appearing in one series, have their analogues in the other. For example: where [ſ (ā) is pronounced [without any gliding of the tongue toward ſ as in Scotch and in Continental pronunciation, you find also that }ł (ō) is pronounced } without the ł glide.

So, too, where individual speakers give [ſ or Ɩſ for [ſ (ā) they also usually say }ł or Ɉł for }ł (ō), etc.

Examine the table of English vowels and you will see that the front and back-round series are nearly complete, and you will recognize at once the importance of Ɩ (ee) and ł (*oo*), for from them the other vowels of their series can be developed by simply enlarging the aperture.

The mixed vowels (ˡ and I) and the back vowels (Ɩ Ɩ and J) present no difficulties, for the following reason: any sort of an indefinite sound will pass for I (*er* in *her*) and ˡ (the sound of the indefinite article *a* in a sentence) differs so slightly from this that there is no need of distinguishing between them. In unaccented syllables I would express these two sounds indiscriminately by (I) the voice sign.

Ɩ (*a* in ask, path, etc.) also differs so slightly from J (*a* in father, calm, etc.) that there is no need to bother a deaf child with the distinction. I teach and write them both as Ɩ and few deaf children have any difficulty in giving the sound.

Then, again, this may be considered as identical with Ɩ. For example: though the vowels in calf and cuff are really different vowels in teaching the deaf, we may consider them as the long and short form of the same vowel, because, as a matter of fact, a deaf child gives Ɩ when he attempts to shorten Ɩ. It should be noted that this vowel Ɩ (*u* in up) like ł (*u* in pull), and Ɉ (*o* in on) never occurs by itself or as a final element. I would not, therefore, teach these sounds elementarily, but always in combination with a succeeding consonant. The short effect should not be produced by a sudden impulse of voice, but by cutting off the sound by the assumption and prolongation of the succeeding consonant. For example: let a child prolong (ɪ)the vowel Ɩ and wind up with a softly uttered Ɛ>, and you get the effect of "calf" (ɑƖƐ = ɑƖɪƐ>). Whereas, let the child attempt to give the same vowel sound, but prolong the Ɛ position, jumping as quickly as possible from the ɑ to the ɜ position and you get the effect of "cuff" (ɑ]ɜ = ɑɹɜ+>.) So with *calm* and *come*. If he tries to give the same vowel sound to both, prolonging the ɘ in the latter word, passing quickly from the ɑ to the ɘ position, you will, as a matter of fact get ɑ]ɘ although he tried to say ɑ]ɘ with a shortened vowel and a prolonged consonant. I find in the case of the other short vowels ɪɟ and ɾ that deaf children generally produce the proper effect by attempting to pronounce them as ɪ ɟ and ɾ, passing quickly over the vowel to the succeeding consonant and prolonging it. Thus if a child pronounces ɒɪω (*pool*) correctly, let him prolong the ω passing as quickly as possible from the ɒ to the ω and he produces the effect of ɒɪω (*pull*). So with the word *foot*. Let him try to pronounce it as ɜɪʊ>, prolonging the shut position ʊ of the *t*, and passing as quickly as possible from the ɜ to the ʊ>, and you get the proper vernacular effect ɜɪʊ>. So with ɟ. You can convert *caught* into *cot* by prolonging the shut position (ʊ) of the *t*, (ʊ>) or *gaud* into *god*, by prolonging the *d* (ʊ.)

The vowel ɾ is the most frequent vowel in the English language. It is rarely necessary, however, to explain to a deaf child that it differs from ɾ in any other respect than length. As a general rule, if the deaf child prolongs the shut position (ʊ) of the *t* (ʊ>) in the word *eat*, passing quickly over the vowel position, the vernacular effect of it is produced (ɾʊ>=ɾʊ+>). Indeed, in all short vowels the succeeding consonant is prolonged.

Mr. Lyon: How would you distinguish the final *y* in words; would you use that same sound?

Dr. Bell: Yes.

Mr. Lyon: In that case you would not have a consonant following.

Dr. Bell: That's true. The other short vowels ɪ ɟ and] are always succeeded by consonants. I think this is also true of ʈ and perhaps of ʈ except when followed by ɪ (*er*). I do not think any of the short vowels excepting ɾ occur as final elements. The correct sound of final *y* is ɾ (*i* in it). As a general rule the pupil will give the effect correctly if he tries to make the sound ɾ (*ee*) carelessly, with little muscular exertion. I, therefore, begin by getting him to try to say ɾ (*ee*) softly. If the effect of ɾ results, well and good. I leave it alone. If, however, we obtain too pronounced an ɾ (ee) I then explain that the aperture is too small. The great trouble is that if you tell a deaf child that ɾ has a larger aperture than ɾ he is apt to exaggerate the difference and give too large an aperture.

Whereas, if you don't say anything at all about the aperture the attempt to say ſ with little muscular exertion usually results in a satisfactory ſ.

I give below a table of the English vowels, as I teach them to the deaf, arranging them so as to show their place in my father's complete vowel system already given.

—	—	ſ	—	—	—
—	—	—	ɿ	—	—
—	—	ɩ	—	ɪ	—
ł	—	—	—	—	—
—	—	—	—	—	—
ɉ	—	—	—	—	—

The short vowels ſ ł ɉ and ɿ, as I have already explained, may be considered as identical with ſ ł ɉ and ɿ, save in exceptional cases, where the organic difference must be explained.

The medium aperture vowels ɩ and ɉ are only used in English as the initial parts of the diphthongs ɩſ (*ā*) and ɉł (*ō*). They are usually so difficult of acquirement that we are generally forced to accept ɩſ and ɉł for ɩſ and ɉł. The distinction of sound is so slight, however, that the error is surely immaterial.

ſ (*ee*) and ł (*oo*) in unaccented syllables become ſ (ĭ) and ł (*ŏŏ*) in ordinary speech. For example: the word *the* by itself is ωſ (thee), but when unaccented becomes ωſ; ωſɵɉſ ωſʊɩſɵω, "thĭ boy, thĭ table," etc. The word *to* by itself is ʊł, but in unaccented positions becomes ʊł, as "I gave a book ʊłωſɵɉſ [tŏŏ thĭ boy]."

We are so accustomed to give indefinite vowels in unaccented syllables that any sort of indefinite vowel effect is more acceptable than a precise pronunciation such as would be given if the syllables were accented. For example: ʊı ωı ɵɉſ (tŭ thŭ boy) rapidly and indefinitely uttered would be more acceptable to ordinary ears than ʊł ωſɵɉſ (too thee boy) precisely uttered. In fact, in all unaccented syllables ı is better than a precise vowel. ſ and ł should be given or ſ and ł, but ı is better than an incorrect ſ or ł.

Mr. Lyon: That does not differ materially from the sound of *u* in up as we usually hear it.

Dr. Bell: It is an indefinite sound, somewhat like that, but more like *er* in her.

Mr. Crouter: Don't we get that effect in the word "carpet" by dropping out the vowels?

DR. BELL: Yes, we can use this indefinite sound (ı) in place of the *r*.

MR. CROUTER: I was not speaking of *r*, but take any case, the consonants may be held together in a word and you pass over from one consonant to the other and this indefinite vowel sound is produced.

DR. BELL: Yes, it usually occurs as a transitional effect. For example: In the last syllable of "carpet" carelessly uttered.

MISS BLACK: What sound do you give the final *y*?

DR. BELL: Give me a word, Miss Black.

MISS BLACK: Well, "Mary."

DR. BELL: ʃ (*i* in it). I would write the word ɘ[ıωʃ, although many Americans say ɘ[rωʃ. When the letter *r* occurs between two vowels, and the first one is long, English usage demands the insertion of voice-glide (ı) between the long vowel and the medial *r*, thus fairy (ɜ[ıωʃ) weary (ɘʃıωʃ) fiery (ɜ]rıωʃ) fury (ɜɒłıωʃ), etc.

When the letter *r* occurs finally or before a consonant, for example—ear, poor, farm, warm, etc.; the *r* (ω) is not pronounced. Even elocutionists demand only a gliding of the tongue toward the position for *r* (ɤ). Thus ʃɤ ɒłɤ ɜ]ɤɘ ɘʄɤɘ etc.

When deaf children, however, attempt to give glide *r* (ɤ), they exaggerate the effect and produce a consonant sound. (ω), thus ʃω ɒłω ɜ]ωɘ ɘʄωɘ, etc.

The effect is at once recognized as peculiar. Defective combinations usually result in such words as ɜ]ωıɘ (farum) ɘʄωıɘ (warum), etc. When the consonant *r* itself is defective, as it often is, for example: ωⁿ or ωᶜ, the effect is so unnatural that it would be better to omit the *r* altogether. Many hearing people fail to give an *r* of any sort in such words as the above, and I would recommend the omission of the glide *r* (ɤ) in teaching the deaf. The voice glide (ı) answers every purpose and is easily uttered. When a deaf child gives that in place of (ɤ) no one but an elocutionist could tell the difference. For example: Let the child give ʃı (ear) ɒłı (poor) ɜ]ıɘ (farm) ɘʄıɘ (warm). Indeed, in the last cases even the voice glide itself may be omitted without any very marked peculiarity. Thus: ɜ]ɘ (fahm) ɘʄɘ (wawm). This surely would be more acceptable than the pronunciation usually given by deaf children, for these words.

When *r* occurs as a final and the next word begins with a vowel, a consonant *r* is usually required. ƨʃ[ı would be to ordinary ears a satisfactory pronunciation of the word "there," but if you put that into a sentence where the next word commences with a vowel (for example, "there is," etc.), then ƧꞮꞮ ꞮƧ would not prove acceptable, and we must introduce a consonant *r* thus ƧꞮꞮɷꞮƧ.

Now it is a difficult thing for a teacher to get a deaf child to say ʘƆƱꞮɣ without an exaggeration of the glide *r* element that produces an unnatural effect, but any child can give ʘƆƱꞮ which is perfectly satisfactory to most ears. If you didn't know there was no *r* there, you would never find it out. I would have the deaf child give simply the indefinite vowel (ꞮꞮ) for the whole syllable *er* in such words.

In English utterance two other glides (ㅈ and ɟ) are employed in the diphthongal vowels.

In forming ㅈ the tongue glides towards the position for ⋂ (*y*) or Ɪ (*ee*); and in forming ɟ the glide is towards the position for ϶ (*w*) or Ɨ (*oo.*) Diphthongal sounds present great difficulties to the deaf and are rarely given correctly. Both the initial and final positions are apt to be wrong, and a strong tendency is manifested to prolong the final instead of the initial part of the diphthong.

My plan of correction is to write what the pupils do, so that they may see the difference between the sounds they actually utter and those we wish them to give.

My father has not provided a sufficient number of glide symbols to enable us to represent the incorrect sounds uttered by our pupils, and I have, therefore, found it advisable to express glides by vowel symbols upon a small scale. This gives us a sufficient number of forms without introducing new symbols. For the deaf I write the diphthongs Ɩㅈ Ɔㅈ Ɉㅈ Ɉɟ Ɔɟ as Ɩɪ Ɔɪ Ɉɪ Ɉɨ Ɔɨ.

The common defect of prolongation of the final element can be expressed as ɩⵎ ɔⵎ ɉⵎ ɉƗ ɔƗ. and when the combination is dis-syllabic this becomes ƖƖ ƆƖ ɈƖ ɈƗ ƆƗ.

In teaching such a diphthong as Ɔɪ, I commence in the following manner:

Say Ɔ. Now say Ɩ. Now ƆƖ ƆƖ ƆƖ, etc.
Now ɔƖ ɔƖ ɔƖ, etc. Now Ɔɪ Ɔɪ Ɔɪ, etc.

Whatever variations occur during the course of the lesson are represented symbolically, and the pupil is requested to repeat them in contrast with the correct sound. Thus: "You said Ɔι. Do it again Ɔι Ɔι Ɔι etc." "Now give Ɔι Ɔɪ Ɔι Ɔɪ etc." "Now you said Ɪɪ. Try it again Ɪι Ɪɪ Ɪɪ etc. Now give Ɔɪ Ɔι Ɪɪ etc."

The principle of correction is: *write what the pupil does, and then get him to repeat the incorrect sound in contrast with the sound you wish him to utter.*

I do not think it is possible to obtain great accuracy of vowel quality without the use of symbols of some sort for incorrect sounds, and the adoption of the principle referred to above. The symbols of visible speech are of great utility for this purpose. Indeed, I believe them to be essential. Without them you can only hope for approximations to the correct vowel positions. Without them your great, and indeed your only reliance must be upon imitation. In any case the power of imitation should be developed by constant practice before a mirror.

I always teach [ſ (*ā*) and Jſ (*ī*) in contrast with one another, so as to make the pupil familiar with the difference. These diphthongs are apt to be pronounced alike as Iſ or ıſ. For example: A pupil will say ıƷıſƱϖıſ, instead of ıƷJſƱϖ[ſ (fine day). For the same reason I teach }ł and Jł in contrast.

In giving Ɉſ, pupils generally give too small an aperture between the lips for the initial position. I think this results chiefly from the spelling (*oi*). They try to give an *ō* followed by short *i*. Indeed, very often the *o* is followed by glide *oo*, thus making a dissyllabic compound something like }łſ. For example: ϴ}łſ (bo-ee) for ϴɈſ (boy).

Sounds that differ only slightly from one another should, I think, be taught together, in contrast, as the best means of securing a distinction. Thus: teach [ſ Jſ and Ɉſ as one group, and }ł and Jł as another.

I would also practice such compounds as [ſı Jſı Ɉſı (vowels in *layer*, *liar* and *lawyer* written ωɈſı or ωɈϭı). }łı Jłı (vowels in *sower* and *sour*). In such words as *sore* and *more* there is no glide. Many persons say Ʊ}ı ϴ}ı. My father would write Ʊ}ɤ ϴ}ɤ, but I should recommend a still larger aperture in teaching the deaf. I would write ƱɈı and ϴɈı (saw-er maw-er) for "sore" and "more," and Ʊ}łı and ϴ}łı (so-er and mo-er) for "sower" (one who sows) and "mower" (one who mows).

It is very difficult to get a deaf child to distinguish Ɩ from Ɩ (*e* in pet, from *a* in pat). It is important, however, that the attempt should be made, as the slight difference of sound often makes a great difference in the sense. For example: Met, mat, bet, bat, etc. The distinction is best obtained, I think, by practice before a mirror.

Vowels are so difficult of acquirement by the deaf with accuracy and precision that we may consider it fortunate that usage tolerates considerable latitude in the pronunciation of these elements.

The precise shade of vowel quality given in one part of the country is not heard in another. Travelers in England are startled by the cry ƆƖɘ ƱI ƆƖɘ ƱI ("Keb, sir, keb, sir,") from the cabmen in London. The Irishman says "oi" for I. Many Americans say ƷɪɪƱƆ> for ƷɪƴƱƆ> (first) and everywhere we hear ɪƚƍɪƚ for ʖƚƍʖƚ (oh, no).

Certain defects are recognized as individual, or family peculiarities of speech; others are characteristic of whole communities and constitute a provincial utterance or dialect· and still others reveal the nationality of the foreigner.

I think I am pretty safe in saying that the "standard pronunciation," like the "average school boy," nowhere exists! We all depart from it in a greater or less degree. Study the character and extent of the variations that exist among educated people and don't be too critical of defects of your pupils if they fall within those limits.

The pronunciation of the consonant elements of speech is so uniform in all English-speaking countries that very slight variations are received as foreign sounds, while greater departures from the standard convey the idea that the vocal organs are themselves defective. People speak of "curing" such defects, as though they were diseases, or the result of malformations, requiring the surgeon's care. Vowel peculiarities, on the other hand, fail to convey this idea and are more suggestive of provincial or foreign utterance.

Small-aperture vowels, like ƚ or ɪ, are given everywhere with substantial uniformity, and any marked deviation from the standard is suggestive of foreign birth. Vowels of larger aperture are constantly mispronounced by the best educated people. Even cultivated Bostonians, for example, sometimes call their own city ɘƆƱƆıƍ (Bahston). Unusual variations from the standard if of slight extent, are suggestive of provincialism, and where the departure is greater the speaker is supposed to be a foreigner.

From this it will be seen that exactitude of pronunciation is more necessary with certain sounds than with others. Consonants and small-aperture vowels in accented syllables must be accurately given; whereas considerable latitude may be allowed in the pronunciation of medium and large-aperture vowels, and of diphthongal sounds wherever they occur. This is fortunate, for these are just the sounds that are most difficult of acquirement with definiteness by our pupils.

I would direct your attention to the very great importance of training a child to retain a position unchanged, until directed to relinquish it. The common practice of pronouncing an element of speech and then immediately relinquishing the position leads the child to consider the relinquishment as an essential feature of the sound. In speaking he relinquishes one position before he assumes the next, thus producing a transitional effect or glide sound between the elements. This sound appears either in a vocal (ı) or non-vocal (>) form, according as the elements themselves are vocal or non-vocal.

Ask the average deaf child to say ɵɪɵɪɵɪ (bee-bee-bee) and you will obtain ɵıɪıɵıɪıɵıɪı. The tongue is raised for ɪ and depressed for ɵ so that it moves up and down for every syllable. Pronounce ɵɪɵɪɵɪ yourself and you will find that the tongue does not move at all but remains continuously in the ɪ position. The movement is entirely labial. This defect of combination runs through all the elements.

The great principle to be kept in mind is that positions do not merely succeed one another like the letters on a printed page, but overlap. A position must be retained until the mouth is in position for the next element.

In teaching the principle of combination to a deaf child, I would recommend you to commence with the vowel ɪ. Get your pupil to prolong ɪ while you open and close his lips with your fingers. At once you get ɵɪɵɪɵɪ. Direct the child's attention to the fact that the tongue remains in the ɪ position all the time, and in fact that it does not move at all. Then get him to manipulate his own lips and then to produce the effect without manipulation. When he can do this well, try ɷɪɷɪ, etc., and the analogy of the symbols will help him to give the correct effect. Let him have the idea of retaining the ɾ position continuously while he moves the point of the tongue. Then try ɑɪɑɪ, etc., retaining the ɪ position while he moves the back of the tongue. The chief difficulties of articulation teaching lie not so much with the elementary sounds as with their combination into syllables. A deaf child may be perfectly able to give every element and yet be unable to utter a sentence that is intelligible to ordinary people.

The most important point, I think, in the whole of articulation teaching is the thorough comprehension by teachers and pupils of the law of combination.

ARTICULATION TEACHING.

I should like in conclusion to say a few words upon the general subject of articulation teaching. We don't know yet how best to teach speech to the deaf. If we did we wouldn't be here. We have come here to learn from one another in the hope of improving our methods of teaching. Now I am inclined to think that the more nearly we can pattern our methods of teaching after the method adopted by nature in teaching speech to hearing children, the better should be our results. It is certainly the case that the methods usually employed in schools for the deaf do not even approximate to the nursery method of the hearing child. Not one of the little hearing children whom you may have left at home commenced by learning elementary sounds. Mothers do not begin with elementary sounds and then combine them into syllables and words. The mother speaks whole sentences even to the infant in arms. The child listens and listens, until a model is established in the mind. Then the child commences to imitate, not elementary sounds, but whole words. Indeed, people grow up to adult life without ever having uttered elementary sounds, and when they do come to study them, it is for the purpose of improving and perfecting their speech. With hearing persons the elements come last, not first. They constitute the final, not the initial, exercises of articulation. I would commend this fact to the serious attention of the members of this Association. The question is often in my mind whether we are not making a radical mistake, and whether it would not be better to commence with sentences and whole words, rather than with elements, and accept imperfect speech from little deaf children as we do from hearing children.

If you copy the natural process, what you want first is the *use* of speech, and then perfect the articulation as the child grows up. In this connection I would commend to your notice the paper of Dr. Greenberger upon the Word Method, which constitutes the first Circular of Information. This is an entire reversal of the position I assumed when I entered upon the work of articulation teaching. But the more I think of it, the more I am convinced that a great principle is involved. Words first and elements afterwards. I recognize, however, that there are real practical difficulties in the way of its application to the deaf. If you once allow a deaf child to speak in a defective manner is there not danger that the defective pronunciation will become habitual? This is a serious objection and should be carefully considered. In the case of the hearing child, a corrective element is always present, he hears. He hears the model pronunciation constantly used by those about him, and also hears his own imperfect babble. His ear forms a medium of comparison whereby he perceives the relation of the sounds he utters to those he desires to make. In the case of the deaf child we might anticipate that a corrective element would also be present if he could see speech as others hear it.

(1) He must see the model pronunciation constantly and clearly repeated so as to fix it in his mind, to take the place of the conversation that goes on in the presence of the hearing child; and

(2) He must see his own imperfect speech so that he may perceive the relation of the sounds he utters to the correct pronunciation.

It may be well to consider how far it may be possible for us to bring about these conditions.

1. Speech-reading fulfills the first condition only in part. The visible movements of the mouth may recall the model pronunciation to the mind of the deaf child, when once acquired, but it does not exhibit the pronunciation with clearness and definiteness to the eye. If we could supplement speech-reading by books and periodicals printed in phonetical type, a great advantage would be gained. In Germany and Italy, where oral methods are most successful, spelling corresponds to pronunciation, and this first condition is, therefore, fulfilled by the ordinary literature of those countries. In English-speaking countries, however, ordinary literature is of comparatively little use in impressing upon the memory of the deaf child the correct pronunciation of the language. Our spelling is so irregular and unphonetical that even hearing people often have to

resort to a dictionary to ascertain how a word should be pronounced. What we most need is reading matter for our pupils in which the words are spelt as they are pronounced. In two hours a deaf child can read as many words as a hearing child hears in the course of a day, and if the spelling only corresponded to the pronunciation, reading would fix the model in his mind, and speech-reading would constantly recall it. Any kind of phonetical alphabet would do for this purpose ; but Visible Speech would be especially advantageous because it would be possible through this agency to fulfill the second condition also.

2. The deaf child must see the relation between the sound he utters and the correct sounds of speech. I know of no other means of accomplishing this end than Visible Speech or the Lyon Manual,—but they will do it.

I think with these agencies we would have a corrective element that would lead to improvement of speech as the child grows up and permit of the adoption of a more natural method of teaching than now exists.

I throw out these thoughts as suggestions merely, for I recognize, of course, the great difficulty of carrying them practically into execution. I would have you, however, appreciate the importance of the principle involved, and consider whether in the face of the difficulties that present themselves, it would be better to abandon the principle, or study the difficulties and attempt to remove them. I think that that method which conforms most nearly to the method whereby hearing children acquire speech, will be most worthy of adoption by teachers of the deaf. With these remarks I shall close. I shall now be glad to answer any questions.

MR. LYON: I would like to know if the symbols on your charts represent the elements to which you would reduce all the English words ?

DR. BELL: Yes. There are some elements not usually considered as English. The German *ch* (C) for instance, and its corresponding vocal (Є). I would recommend that those should be taught to every deaf child, because they enter into the composition of Ɔ (*wh*) and ł (*oo*) and, indeed, form the key to the English vowels.

MR. LYON: I notice that the glide *r* is omitted.

DR. BELL: Yes. And I consider that as a very important matter. I have found it a very difficult thing to get glide *r* from a deaf child without gross exaggeration of the movement of the tongue, and I consider it entirely unnecessary to bother him about it. I would recommend substituting for glide *r* a mere indefinite murmur of the voice (1). If you give that to a deaf child in place of glide *r* you will get something which passes current for good speech, although there is no suspicion of an *r* about it.

MR. LYON: I see in the symbols that the indefinite position represents voice glide. Is it the same thing?

DR. BELL: The same thing. What I mean to say is, that when we give a deaf child the indefinite voice mark in place of glide *r*, we obtain from him a sound that approximates very closely to the vernacular effect.

MISS YALE: I believe in Dr. Bell's theory thoroughly.

VOWEL THEORIES.

BY ALEXANDER GRAHAM BELL.

Read before the National Academy of Arts and Sciences, April 15, 1879, and reprinted from the American Journal of Otology, Vol. I., July, 1879.

Hemholtz has shown that an educated ear perceives a combination of musical tones where an uneducated ear supposes a single sound; and his theory, that the feeble, usually unheard, musical tones are the cause of the peculiar sensation we term the "quality" of a sound, seems now to be universally accepted as correct.

According to this theory, a vowel is a musical compound, consisting of a mixture of musical tones of different pitches and various intensities. The lowest, or fundamental tone, gives the pitch to the whole, and is determined by the rate of vibration of the vocal cords.

It is certainly the case that an attentive ear can perceive, in every vowel uttered, a number of distinct musical sounds; but the hypothesis that the ear perceives them *only*, and that it is unable to appreciate the quality of the vowel directly, should be received with caution. According to Helmholtz, the human ear is incapable of perceiving any other than simple pendular vibrations, and it is therefore under the necessity of splitting up a vowel into its constituent musical elements before it can perceive its quality.

Thus Helmholz holds that vowels are *inferred* from the presence of certain musical tones, and that they do not give rise in the ear to distinct sensations of their own.

The rods of Corti are supposed by him to analyze the vibrations imparted to the liquid of the internal ear, so as to split them up into the pendular motions of which they are theoretically composed; but it cannot be received as proven that the simultaneous vibration of certain of these rods gives rise to the perception of the quality of a sound; for Pritchard and other comparative anatomists have shown that the rods of Corti are entirely wanting in parrots and other birds that imitate and therefore perceive the sounds of speech.

Whether or not, however, there exists in the human ear an apparatus for taking direct cognizance of the quality of a sound, Helmholtz has proved, by the synthesis of vowel sounds, that there exists the most intimate relation between certain combinations of musical tones and the quality of a sound. Not only are such tones audible whenever a vowel is produced, but the converse is equally true; and we may therefore assume, at least as a working hypothesis, that vowels are compound musical tones. I shall follow the example of Ellis[1] in terming the musical constituents of vowel sounds, "partial" tones, to designate their subordination to the compound as a whole.

The illustrations of vowel-synthesis given by Helmholtz show vowels composed of tones whose frequencies are multiples of the fundamental and the question arises: "*Are the upper partial tones, which are characteristic of vowel sounds, invariably harmonics of the fundamental of the voice, or are they independent of it?*"

Again: "*If they are harmonics, do they uniformly bear the same relation to the fundamental, whatever the pitch of the voice may be?*"

These questions at first sight seem to receive different answers, accordingly as we attempt to solve the problem (1) from a consideration of the organic formation of the vowel sounds, or from an examination of the records, (2) of the phonautograph, and (3) of the phonograph. The results common to all three methods of investigation, however, point to a theory of vowel sounds in close accordance with the ideas of Helmholtz, as expressed by Ellis in his "Early English Pronunciation," Part IV., p. 1277.

In examining these questions, it may be convenient to designate, by distinct names, two varieties of Helmholtz's vowel theory, concerning which there has been of late considerable discussion:

The fixed pitch hypothesis.—The upper partial tones characteristic of vowel sounds may be supposed to have fixed, invariable pitches, and the element of pitch may be considered the distinguishing feature.

The harmonic hypothesis.—According to this hypothesis, the upper partial tones characteristic of vowels are always harmonics of the fundamental, varying in pitch with it, the vowel characteristic lying in the predominance of certain harmonics.

As an illustration of the difference between these hypotheses, let us consider for a moment the musical composition of the vowel ō.

Helmholtz states that he produced a very fine ō by combining the sounds of certain tuning-forks whose rates of vibration were multiples of that of the lowest fork. The prime tone was $B_\flat$; the 2d, 3d, and 5th forks were allowed to sound feebly, and the sound of the 4th fork was brought out much more strongly. In this experiment, then, the characteristic tone ($b_\flat'$) was the double octave of the fundamental. Now, if the fixed pitch hypothesis be correct, the vowel ō should always be distinguished by a partial tone of the ($b_\flat'$); whereas, if the harmonic hypothesis be correct, the predominant partial should vary in pitch with the pitch of the voice, and be always its double octave.

I. *Vowel Theories, considered in Relation to the Organic Formation of Vowel Sounds.*[2]

When we examine the vocal organs we find numerous cavities located in the thorax, larynx, pharynx, nares, and in the mouth. The air in

---

[1] The phraseology of Ellis will be used throughout this paper. For definitions, etc., see Ellis's translation, "The Sensations of Tone," footnote to page 36.

[2] In all references to the organic formation of speech sounds, I adopt the phraseology of Melville Bell. For definitions, etc., see "Visible Speech: The Science of Universal Alphabetics."

each cavity has a tendency towards a definite rate of vibration, and when agitated in any way produces its resonance tone.

In the act of speech the air is set in vibration in all these cavities, the resonance tones of the cavities mingle with the tones due to the vibration of the vocal cords, and thus produce the complex sounds of human speech. The movements of the tongue, lips, etc., modify the shape and size of some of these resonance cavities, and thus enable us to produce sounds the musical constituents of which are almost infinitely variable at will. The constant cavities of the vocal organs, the shapes of which are determined by nature, and are therefore independent of will, probably give to the speaker's voice that individuality of tone that enables us to pick out the voice of one speaker from a multitude of others, while the variable cavities give prominence to partials that characterize the elements of spoken language.

The cavities of the mouth are chiefly concerned in the production of vowel quality. When a vowel position is assumed by the vocal organs, the mouth-passage is slightly constricted at some particular part (see Fig. 1), and thus two resonance cavities, *a* and *b*, are estab-

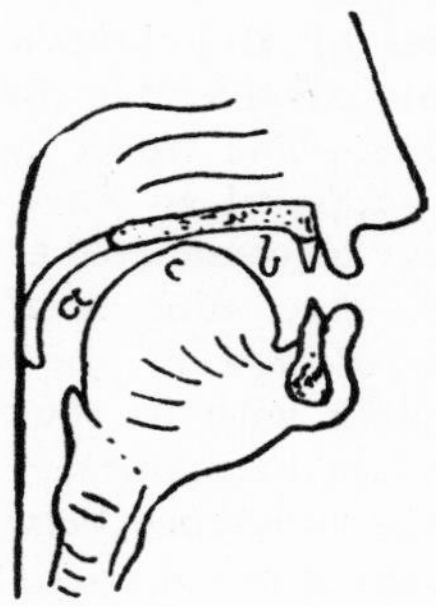

FIG. 1.

lished, the interior of the mouth somewhat resembling in shape the interior of a chamber formed by placing two bottles neck to neck, the two resonance chambers being represented by the bodies of the bottles, and the constricted passage between them by the necks.

I have found that the resonance tones of these cavities can be readily studied in the following manner:

To Study the Pitch of the Posterior Cavity:

Close the glottis, assume the vowel position, and tap gently against the throat with the thumb-nail. (A sound will be perceived somewhat similar to that produced by tapping against the side of an empty bottle). A double pitch will be noticed, but the tone due to the posterior cavity, *a*, will be much more fully produced than that due to the other. I have succeeded in making the sound audible to large audiences by placing the forefinger of the left hand against the throat. and tapping it very forcibly with the thumb-nail of the right hand.

A loud sound can also be produced by striking a piece of wood or cork held against the throat.

To Study the Pitch of the Anterior Cavity:

Close the glottis, assume the vowel position, and strike gently a piece of wood, or cork, held in front of the mouth or against the cheek. I have found that an ordinary lead-pencil, held firmly against one side of the mouth, readily yields the resonance tone of the mouth cavity when struck with the thumb-nail. A double tone can be perceived, but that due to the anterior cavity is much more prominent than the other.

The tone due to the anterior cavity may be studied alone, by depressing the soft palate until it touches the back of the tongue. (This is the position for "ng" in the word "sing.") Under such circumstances the soft palate cuts off all communication with the air in the posterior cavity, and a single resonance accompanies each vowel position. When the absolute pitch of the anterior cavity is sought, the former method is preferable, as the depression of the soft palate alters the tone.

The tones of the cavities are best brought out by contrast. For instance, assume successively the positions for certain vowels, and observe the series of tones produced, first by the anterior cavity and then by the posterior cavity. The difference will be found to be very striking.

When the vowel positions are assumed in the order shown by Melville Bell, in his "Visible Speech," the tones of the cavities are found to be arranged in regular musical sequence. For instance, commencing with the high-front vowel (ee), assume successively the positions for the other vowels of the front group. A double series of resonances will be obtained, so arranged that the tones of one series fall in pitch while the tones of the other rise. *The same remark is true for all the organic groups of unrounded vowels. The pitch of the anterior cavity falls in pitch as the vowel aperture is enlarged, and that of the posterior cavity rises.* It is different, however, with rounded vowels. For instance, take the high-front-round vowel, (ü in German), and assume successively the positions for all the vowels of that group down to the low-front-wide-round vowel. *The resonance tones of the anterior and posterior cavities both rise in pitch as the vowel aperture is enlarged. All the groups of rounded vowels behave in a similar manner.*

Again, compare unrounded vowels of similar aperture, but of different organic formations. For instance, assume successively the high-front, high-mixed, and high-back vowel positions: the pitch of the anterior cavity falls and the pitch of the posterior rises. The same thing occurs when we compare the mid-front, mid-mixed, and mid-back vowels, or the low-front, low-mixed, and low-back vowels.

Comparing in like manner rounded vowels of similar aperture, but of different organic formation, the same fact is noticed, namely, that *the further back in the mouth the point of constriction is located, the lower is the pitch of the anterior cavity and the higher the pitch of the posterior.*

Comparing rounded and unrounded vowels of the same organic formation and aperture, as, for instance, the high-front vowel (ēē) with the high-front-rounded vowel (ü in German): the pitch of the posterior cavity is the same for both vowels; but the pitch of the anterior is lower for the rounded (ü) than for the unrounded vowel (ee).

The changes of pitch produced in the anterior and posterior cavities of the mouth become intelligible by reference to familiar facts of resonance. Thus blow across the mouth of an empty bottle, and its resonance tone can be perceived in the rustling sound caused by the breath. Pour water into the bottle, and the pitch of the tone becomes higher. Place your fingers over the mouth of the bottle, so as to reduce the size of the opening, and the pitch falls.

It will thus be seen that the pitch of a cavity falls when its interior capacity is increased, and also when the exterior orifice is contracted.

The depression of the tongue (see Fig. 1) should, therefore, cause an elevation of the pitch of cavity *a*, and a lowering of that of cavity *b*; for the air space in cavity *b* becomes larger when the tongue is depressed; and the width of the exterior opening (*c*) of cavity *a* is at the same time increased.

Every position assumed by the vocal orgaus determines the shape and size of the cavities of the mouth, and thus determines the absolute pitch of the resonance tones proper to those cavities.

When air is passed through the mouth, as in the act of speech, a new element enters into the inquiry: Is vowel quality due to the mouth position assumed by the organs, or is it caused by the vibration of the vocal cords? If the former, we would expect that the characteristic upper partials would bear some relation to the resonance tones proper to the mouth cavities and be independent of the pitch of the voice. If the latter, we would expect them to bear some relation to the pitch of the voice and be independent of the pitch of the mouth cavities.

The mere passage of air through the mouth is sufficient to bring out the characteristic tones of the mouth-cavities. Vowel quality is audible in a whisper, and can even be produced by forcing air into the mouth by means of a pair of bellows.

It should be noted, in this connection, that vowels are generally preceded in actual utterance by elements that approximate very closely to consonants in their organic formation; "initial vowels" being preceded by the throat-shut consonant—an element belonging to the same general class as P—T—K, but for which we have no letter in the English language.

Consonants result from obstructive positions of the vocal organs. During the utterance of speech the air in the thorax is continually compressed by the action of the abdominal muscles, diaphragm, and muscles of the thorax, so that when the emission of breath is momentarily checked by the formation of some obstructive position, the cavities behind the point of constriction become inflated.

Thus, when a vowel is preceded by a consonant—a sudden puff of air accompanies the relinquishment of the consonantal position—and this puff, passing through the vowel-configuration, is sufficient to bring out the characteristic tones of one or more of the vowel-cavities quite independently of the vibration of the vocal cords.

An interesting case may be mentioned which bears upon this point. Dr. Moore, of Rochester, N. Y., had a patient whose glottis had become closed by disease. For twenty-five years the man had been dependent for life upon air supplied through a tube inserted in the *trachea*. He could speak, although no particle of air could be forced into the mouth from the lungs. His speech was perfectly intelligible, distinct, and even loud, but of course peculiar, on account of the absence of voice. He could not pronounce vowel sounds by themselves, but they were distinctly audible when preceded by consonants. By long practice the man had acquired the power of contracting and expanding the cavity at the back part of the mouth to a wonderful extent. The air which was moulded into speech was alternately drawn into this cavity and expelled from it by the forcible action of the muscles of the pharynx, soft palate, and back part of the tongue. The cavity seemed to be continually in a state of change—alternately expanding and contracting during the whole progress of his articulation—so that the man could speak for any length of time without pausing for breath ! There seemed, however, to be an instinctive remembrance of the connection between breathing and speech, for he was in the habit of expelling air through the tracheal tube while he was speaking, and of remaining silent when he drew air into the lungs.

Another curious case has been made public by Dr. Moore.[1]

A patient had attempted suicide by cutting his throat. The epiglottis was severed trom the larynx, and, when the man attempted to articulate with his head thrown back, the air passed out through the opening in his throat instead of through the mouth. Under these circumstances the man could pronounce intelligibly certain vowel sounds. Dr. Moore satisfied himself and other observers that there was no passage of air through the mouth, by artificially closing the aperture between the epiglottis and back of the pharynx.

Dr. Moore argued from this experiment that the vowels heard were produced in the larynx instead of in the mouth. This position, however, seems to be untenable ; for the mouth positions for these vowels might have been assumed during the production of the sounds, and the tones of the mouth cavities would be brought out by sympathetic resonance without the necessity of passing air directly through the mouth.

In whistling, the resonance tone of the anterior cavity is brought out so loudly as to constitute a clearly recognizable musical tone. A careful observer will find that his tongue assumes a definite position for each note whistled, and a person can be made to whistle an air unintentionally by making him attempt to whistle certain vowels in succession. In whistling, it seems necessary that the constricted passage in the mouth should be much more narrowed than in actual articulation, and that the anterior orifice should also be small.

Sing such a vowel as ō and gradually contract the passage between the back of the tougue and the soft palate. The resonance tone of ō will be observed to grow in intensity as the passage is contracted, until finally the vowel is converted into a vocalized whistle. By labializing the various vowel positions, the resonance tone of the anterior cavity can be brought into great prominence, and a whistle produced of definite fixed pitch for each vowel-position.

---

[1] See Trans. N. Y. State Medical Society for 1872.

It is found that the pitch of the voice can be varied without appreciably affecting the pitch of the vowel-whistle. It is certainly difficult to bring out the whistle of ōō or ō upon certain pitches of the voice, but the high-front and high-mixed vowels labialized can be easily retained in a whistling condition while the voice glides upwards or downwards.

In studying the double resonance of the mouth-cavity, I have been led to the belief that the fundamental of the anterior cavity is much more essential to the production of vowel quality than that of the posterior.

If we prolong the sound of the voice, and study the effect of the movement of the different vocal organs in modifying the quality of the resultant sound, the attention will be arrested by the fact that movements of the organs further forward than the back of the tongue produce changes of vowel quality, but that motions of the parts behind the back of the tongue do not. The motions of such parts produce quite as marked, if not *more* marked, changes of quality than in the former case; but the resultant sounds would not ordinarily be designated as vowel variations. We should rather speak of them as changes in the *quality* of the voice. For instance, the depression of the soft palate produces a nasal effect, and the movement of the base of the tongue towards the back of the pharynx produces a "guttural" quality of voice.

If the passage between the base of the tongue and the back of the pharynx be contracted laterally, by approximation of the posterior pillars of the soft palate (shown by dotted lines in Fig. 2), a very curious change

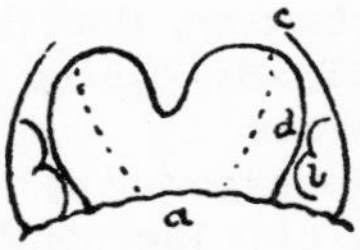

FIG. 2.

of quality is produced. The voice acquires a metallic ring, somewhat like the tone of a brass wind instrument. When the posterior pillars of the soft palate approximate so closely as almost to touch, a very disagreeable reedy quality of voice results, which can perhaps be best described as a sort of "Punch-and-Judy" effect.

When these various motions are produced while a vowel position is assumed, the pitch of the posterior vowel cavity is affected, and the quality of voice accompanying the vowel is changed, but not the vowel itself.

From this it seems evident that the anterior cavity is more important in determining the vowel quality than the posterior cavity.

An examination of the mechanism of speech leaves the mind decidedly biased in favor of the fixed pitch theory of vowel sounds.

II. *Vowel Theories, considered in the Light of Experiments with the Phonautograph.*

If the harmonic hypothesis be correct, and vowels are composed of partial tones whose frequencies are multiples of that of the fundamental of the voice, we should expect, from the researches of Fourier, that the tracings obtained from the phonautograph for vowel sounds should be invariably periodic curves, whatever the pitch of the voice might be. Whereas, if the fixed pitch hypothesis be correct, vowels should not yield periodic curves when tones of voice are used which do not contain the fundamentals of the mouth cavities amongst their harmonics.

Furthermore, if the harmonic theory be correct, the predominant partial tones, bearing always a fixed ratio to the fundamental in pitch and loudness, should produce for each vowel sound a definite form or forms of curve, which should be constant for the same vowels under different pitches of the voice.

Early in 1874 I carried on a series of experiments with an improved form of phonautograph devised by Mr. Charles A. Morey, of the Institute of Technology, in Boston. Vowel sounds were sung to various pitches, and their tracings preserved for study and comparison. The results were briefly as follows:

1. Vowel sounds uniformly produced periodic curves, whatever pitch of voice was employed.

2. The form of vibration was not a constant characteristic.

3. Different vowels sung to different pitches often seem to produce similar curves.

4. Different vowels sung to the same pitch traced curves of different shapes, but they were not sufficiently marked to enable the vowels to be certainly identified.

5. There seemed to be a relation between the complexity of the tracing and the vowel aperture; close aperture vowels yielding curves that approximated very closely to simple pendular vibrations.

Thinking that the results obtained with Mr. Morey's phonautograph might be influenced by the imperfection of the apparatus employed, I tried the tympanic membrane of a human ear as a phonautograph. Dr. Clarence J. Blake, of Boston, suggested this idea, and kindly prepared a specimen for me, with which I carried on experiments. The tympanic membrane and the ossicula were moistened with glycerine and water, and a stylus of hay attached to the incus enabled me to obtain tracings of vowel vibrations on sheets of smoked glass passed rapidly underneath. The results obtained with this apparatus were similar to those obtained with Mr. Morey's phonautograph, and I found it impossible to recognize the various vowel sounds by their tracings. I do not know the full results obtained by Prof. Eli W. Blake with his photographic phonautograph, but all the vowel curves drawn by him, that I have seen, were periodic curves, and seemed to support the conclusions noted above. The general indications of all forms of phonautograph seem to favor the harmonic hypothesis much more than the other. The unstable character of the vibration-forms might be explained by supposing the phases of the harmonic partials to have varied at different times; for Helmholtz has shown that the phases of the upper partial tones are immaterial to the perception of vowel quality.

III. *Vowel Theories considered in the Light of Recent Experiments with the Phonograph.*

Mr. Edison's phonograph furnishes us with an instrument which fortunately can be utilized in the solution of acoustical problems that had before seemed insoluble by experimental methods. I believe that this instrument can be employed as a means of ascertaining the truth or falsity of the harmonic hypothesis.

If the differences of vibration-forms obtained by the phonautograph for the same vowel, at different pitches, merely indicated a difference of phase of the upper partials—the same harmonics being predominant at each pitch of the voice—then, if the relative phases of the harmonic partials could be retained when the pitch of the voice was changed, the same vowel at different pitches should be characterized by the same curve; and a vibration of uniform shape impressed upon the tinfoil of the phonograph should produce the same quality of vowel, whatever the speed of rotation of the cylinder might be.

If, on the other hand, my observations with the phonautograph were correct, that different vowels could be found, which, when sung to different pitches, produced the same tracing, then a vowel sung to the phonograph, while the cylinder is turned at a certain rate of speed, should be reproduced by the instrument as a different vowel when the speed was changed.

When Mr. Preece exhibited the phonograph before the Physical Society of London, on the 2d of March, 1878, I suggested that this experiment should be tried, and stated my belief that the quality as well as the pitch of a vowel would be affected by the speed at which the cylinder was turned. The experiment was at once made, and the results were apparently as I had anticipated. (See *Nature*, Vol. XVII., p. 415.)

Prof. Fleeming Jenkin and Prof. J. A. Ewing about the same time performed a similar experiment in Edinburgh, but arrived at quite different results. They stated, in a letter, dated March 11th, 1878, that "the pitch is, of course, altered, but the vowel sounds retain their quality when the barrel of the phonograph is turned at very different rates. We have made this experiment at speeds varying from about three to one, and we can detect no alteration in the quality of the sounds." (See *Nature*, Vol. XVII., p. 384.)

Such a result determined me to repeat the experiment carefully and at leisure. Mr. Stroh, the eminent mechanician of Hampstead Road, London, kindly permitted me to use his automatic phonograph, the cylinder of which was moved by clock-work. Mr. Alexander J. Ellis was present, and assisted during the experiments.

We found it extremely difficult to use the phonograph in the observation of minute phonetical distinctions. While we differed in our appreciation of some of the effects produced, we agreed in thinking that vowel quality was affected to some extent by the speed of rotation; but we were unable to determine either the amount or the nature of the change. Among other results of these experiments, the vowels in the words mēan, māne, mĕn were often reproduced to my ear as approximately the vowels in mōon, mōan, mŏrn; the reproduced ēē sounding to me as an extremely faint ōō. Mr. Ellis, however, could not agree with me in this conclusion, although he admitted that the quality of these vowels was changed in the reproduction.

The results of our experiments were communicated to *Nature* by Mr. Ellis, in a letter, dated the 3d of April, 1878. (See Vol. XVII., p. 485.)

Dr. Clarence J. Blake, of Boston, and Prof. Cross, of the Institute of Technology, in the same city, were as much struck as I had been by the statements made by Fleeming Jenkin and J. A. Ewing concerning the fixity of vowel quality under varying speeds of rotation, and repeated the experiments alluded to. Very striking differences of vowel quality were perceived by them. Prof. Cross communicated the results to *Nature*, in a letter, dated Boston, April 29th, 1878. (See Vol. XVIII., p. 93.)

This called forth a response from Edinburgh, dated May 29th, 1878. Fleeming Jenkin and J. A. Ewing modified their former statements concerning the fixity of vowel quality, but stated that "the five vowels *a*, *e*, *i*, *o*, *u* (Italian), pronounced in succession are, by contrast at least, thoroughly distinguishable when the instrument is run at various speeds, such as to reproduce the sounds at all the pitches within the compass of the average human voice. That no marked change is produced in the relative values of the vowels is confirmed by the fact that neither in public nor private exhibitions do the hearers of sentences, alternately run slow and fast, suggest that the vowels have changed with a change of speed. . . . We do not, however, think that our instrument speaks with sufficient distinctness to warrant our expressing an opinion as to the constancy of quality of any single vowel when the instrument is run at various speeds." (See *Nature*, Vol. XVIII., p. 167.)

Since the publication of this letter no notice seems to have been taken of this most interesting subject until quite recently, when Mr. Preece and Mr. Stroh revived the discussion in *The Electrician*, for March 29, 1879. Amongst other results they observed that the vowel *āh* is converted by a slow rotation into ō, and that the converse is equally true. This fact has also been independently discovered in America by Mr. Francis Blake and myself.

I have at various times, during the past few months, made experiments with phonographs of different kinds to determine the question of vowel change or fixity; and all the instruments have answered the question of vowel fixity, under changing speeds of rotation, in the negative.

Some experiments made by Mr. Francis Blake and myself, on the fifteenth day of March, 1879, not only demonstrated that vowel quality *does* change under varying speeds of rotation of the cylinder of the phonograph, but also manifested the direction and nature of the change.

The ordinary mode of conducting the experiment previously, was as follows:

A vowel was sung to the phonograph while the cylinder was turned at a uniform rate of speed. The sound was then reproduced from the instrument, while the barrel was turned at a uniform, but different rate of speed. When the experiment was conducted in this way, the change of vowel quality was not marked, and very uncertain results were obtained.

The experiment was now varied as follows:

A vowel was sung into the phonograh in a high-pitched voice, while the cylinder was turned at a uniform but high rate of speed. When the sound was reproduced, the cylinder was started at a high rate of speed and allowed to come gradually to rest. At once the nature of the vowel change became manifest. The vowel *āh* changed by insensible degrees to *awe*, *oh*, and finally *ōō*. (The same effect can be produced by gradually contracting and "rounding" the orifice between the lips, while at the same time the back of the tongue is slightly raised.)

The vowel ēē was gradually converted into the German vowel ü. I am perfectly sure of the labial element of this change, but am uncertain whether there was not also a change in the lingual element. The reproduction was very faint, but to my ear the vowel finally produced was either the "high-front-round" or the "high-mixed-round" vowel.

The dipthongal vowel ī long was reproduced approximately as "ow" in "now." The exact reproduction seemed to be as follows: The initial sound was the "low-back-wide-round" vowel, gliding finally to "high-mixed-round."

A long series of experiments with various vowels satisfied us that the reduction of the speed of rotation below the original rate at which the cylinder was turned, occasions an effect analogous to that produced by labializing the original sound.

It was also evident that there was a lingual element of change, especially when vowels of the "front" and "mixed" series were tried; but it was extremely difficult to locate the resultant sounds. The fixed pitch hypothesis offers a clear understanding of the nature of the change.

With decreasing speed of rotation, the prime tone and the characteristic upper partials fall simultaneously in pitch. Upon our theory the characteristic partials correspond to the fundamentals of the cavities formed in the mouth by assuming some position of the vocal organs. Hence we might expect that as the speed of rotation decreased, the sound produced would correspond to a vowel having anterior and posterior cavities of lower pitch than the original one.

The pitch of the anterior cavity can be lowered by gradually approximating and rounding the lips, and the pitch of the posterior cavity can be similarly changed by contracting the passage between the two cavities. The change of vowel quality produced by decreasing the speed of rotation of the cylinder of the phonograph thus seems to correspond to the change produced by gradually elevating the tongue in the mouth and at the same time contracting and rounding the orifice between the lips.

Effect of Increasing the Speed of Rotation.

A vowel was sung into the phonograph, in a low-pitched voice, while the cylinder was turned very slowly. When the sound was reproduced, the cylinder was started slowly, and the rate of rotation gradually increased.

The vowel *āh* changed gradually to ā in ask, and then to ă (in the word măn). This change of vowel effect was accompanied by a remarkable change in the quality of the reproduced voice. The sound was accompanied by a metallic twang. This disagreeable quality became more and more marked as the speed of rotation was increased, until a sort of "Punch and Judy" squeak was produced.

Upon the fixed pitch hypothesis this change also becomes intelligible.

Organically considered, the change corresponds to a gradual contraction of the posterior cavity, accomplished by approximation of the posterior pillars of the soft palate (as in Fig. 2), accompanied by a gliding forward of the lingual position. This is exactly what one would expect upon the supposition that the posterior and anterior cavities were of higher pitch than in the original vowel.

I was surprised at first that I could detect no tendency in ā (in aim) or ĕ (in mĕn) to glide upwards towards ēē (in sēē), for the anterior cavity in ēē is of smaller size and higher pitch than in the other vowels mentioned; but I now see that the elevation of the tongue would tend to lower the pitch of the posterior cavity, which should theoretically be raised simultaneously with the elevation of the pitch of the anterior cavity.

Results obtained by Fleeming Jenkin and J. A. Ewing.

Jenkin and Ewing have made a minute analysis of the records impressed upon the tinfoil of the phonograph by vowel sounds, and have published the results of their researches in the columns of *Nature*, and in the Transactions of the Edinburgh Royal Society for 1878.

Their analysis of the records of the vowel ō brought out the fact that, whatever pitch of voice was employed, the predominant partial was $b'_\flat$, as fixed by Helmholtz, or within a few notes of that pitch.

As the final result of their researches, Jenkin and J. A. Ewing say (see *Nature*, Vol. XVIII., p. 455): "We are thus brought back to our original statement, that in distinguishing vowels the ear is aided by two factors—one depending on the harmony or group of partials, and the other on the absolute pitch of the constituents. . . . . We are forced to the conclusion, already adopted by Helmholtz and Donders, that the ear recognizes the kind of cavity by which the reinforcement is produced; that, although the sounds which issue differ so much that we fail, when they are graphically represented and mathematically analyzed, to grasp any one prominent common feature, nevetheless, by long practice, the ear is able to distinguish between the different sorts of cavities which are formed in pronouncing given vowels."

General Results.

Of the two hypotheses with which we started, it is certain that one (the harmonic) is wrong and the other only partly right. The balance of evidence inclines largely towards the fixed pitch hypothesis, the main argument against it being found in the periodic curves of the phonautograph.

The solution of the difficulty seems to be that suggested by Ellis, namely, that, "what we call our vowels are not individuals, scarcely species, but rather genera, existing roughly in the speaker's intention, but at present mainly artificially constituted by the habits of writing and reading." (See "Early English Pronunciation," Part IV., p. 1279.)

I do not doubt that the distinguishing characteristic of the vowel-individual, if we could examine it critically, would be found to consist in the presence of partial tones of fixed pitch corresponding to the resonance cavities of some definite fixed position of the vocal organs. A resonance cavity, however, is found to be capable of reinforcing not only a tone corresponding to its fundamental or proper tone, but other tones that differ slightly in pitch from that.

The reinforcement is greater or less as the exciting tone is more or less removed in pitch from the proper tone of the cavity. Thus, when a vowel is sung or spoken, those harmonics of the voice which are nearest in pitch to the proper tones of the mouth cavities would be reinforced at the expense of the proper tones themselves. And although the ear may be guided in its recognition of vowel quality by a feeling of absolute pitch, the vowels would be recognized from the presence of partials of slightly different pitch—the ear locating, as it were, the distance of the fixed pitch by the loudness of the reinforced harmonic.

In ordinary speech the voice is rarely on a level, but is constantly gliding upwards or downwards. When a vowel is spoken, the pitch of the voice is constantly changing. The reinforced partials must also change in pitch, swelling and dying away in intensity, as they approach or recede from the proper pitches of the mouth cavities. Thus, in the rapid succession of reinforced partial tones, accompanying an inflection of the voice, a point of maximum resonance should be perceived having the absolute pitch characteristic of the vowel uttered.[1]

Treating vowels as we find them, as *genera* of sounds, instead of individuals, the most plausible theory seems to be what we may term "the harmonic fixed pitch theory of vowel sounds," according to which a vowel is a musical compound, of partial tones, whose frequencies are multiples of the fundamental of the voice; the predominant partials being always those that are nearest in pitch to the resonance cavities formed in the mouth by the position of the vocal organs assumed during the utterance of the vowel.

---

[1] It is well known that the duration of a v wel is an element in determining its quality. It is extremely difficult to detect the quality of short vowels, and they are often spoken of as "obscure."

INDEX.

DATE DUE

CMSU NOV 17 1975

GAYLORD PRINTED IN U.S.A.